NO PLACE TO PEE

by

DÄCH PHILLUPS

PAGE PUBLISHING, INC.
New York, NY

First originally published by Page Publishing, Inc. 2017

ISBN 978-1-64027-053-4 (Paperback)
ISBN 978-1-64027-054-1 (Digital)

Printed in the United States of America

The Yin and the Yang

They say that beauty is in the eye of the beholder. To me, she was the most beautiful thing that I had ever seen. I came to see her this way even though she wasn't my first choice. I had wanted something more. I was like most men; I wanted to show off, but over time, I realized what folly that is.

The first time I saw her was in Dog Trot, Alabama, many years before, when I went to see a friend. Now it was time for me to go get her and bring her home. I was going to bring her brother home too. I didn't mind; in fact, I was elated to have them both coming to my house to reside with me for the rest of my life at least.

She still looked exactly the same as the first time I saw her and I was in love. We were almost exactly the same age, but the difference in us was that she had been pampered and had spent most of her time indoors. It was the same for her brother.

Her name was Maggie, which I figured on changing. That's what her owner called her. Yes, her owner. She was a pristine 1956 aquamarine blue 1500 MGA. Her brother was an MG ZB Magnette which the owner called Zeb—Zeb was a fine name that I wouldn't change.

I had had other MGs and I had always wanted a Jaguar, but I never made enough money for that. The two beauties that I just bought would have still been out of my reach, but sometimes things just happen, or at least that's how it seems.

Sometimes the wheels of fortune are set in motion generations ahead, and without looking back, we have no real understanding of how things do happen. But without one event, there cannot be another. Life sometimes seems like a tedious and pointless ride, but tearing down a country road in a 1956 1500 MGA sets the mind to understand that the ride doesn't always have to have a point and "meaning" is vastly overrated.

So I have my lady friend with me and a suitable set of tools and some extra coolant for the car. We're heading to Birmingham, Alabama, to see if I can connect with my past. I want to see where my grandfather took the turn in the road that led to me.

I have no idea what I will find or how I will feel, but I have discovered that the closer to the end I am, the more I want to revisit the beginning. When I was a youngster, I thought that nostalgia was bunk; it got in the way of living. But now, nostalgia does seem to be "living."

I saw it in my parents' eyes—that faraway look whenever they talked about the past. My grandparents' too. They are all gone now, so it's my turn for others to see that faraway look in me.

PART I
Into the Dark

He was no philosopher; it was pitch black and there was a boulder lying across his broken leg. He did know, however, that he wished he was somewhere else. He knew that if his father had not died that he would not be here. That practically crapped out sorry farm that he had to leave because of that death looked very appealing to the young man right now.

His circumstances sent his mind reeling. It was his father's brother's idea that brought him into this blasted coal mine. It was his mother's desperation that sealed his fate. It was the fact that he had to quit school in the third grade to work on that sorry farm to help his father feed the family of ten children that created a longing for a better life. Even though he was not given a choice, he wanted to believe that mining was a thousand times better and that farming was only fit for the poorest, stupidest people on earth. Cave-ins and giant boulders will change a fellow's mind in a hurry.

The "Great War" was close to getting started and everybody needed coal. So American companies obliged the Europeans. They sold to the English to make weapons to kill Germans. They also thought it was a capital idea to sell to the Germans so that they could make weapons to kill English! They didn't care. It was money; it spent the same.

This collective insanity brought many people off the farms and into the mines, including this fifteen-year-old boy who was told that he was now a man. He didn't give a rat's ass about the English or the Germans, especially now that he was pinned down in utter darkness, in pain and fearing for his life.

The dust agonizingly clogged his lungs, and other than trying to cough it out, without magnifying the pain of his leg, the only sound he heard was the moans of a fellow miner. He tried to look in the poor man's direction but his lamp was out. The moans stopped and he knew that he was dead.

Was he to die next or was he already dead? Would they get him out? Could they get him out? He tried to pull himself out from under the rock, but the explosion of pain that followed nearly made him pass out.

"Jesus! Please help me!" he cried as he slumped submissively.

He wanted to cry, just as he wanted to cry when he saw his father's lifeless eyes staring into a great void. But he wouldn't; he couldn't. He hadn't since he was a toddler, and by God, he wasn't going to now! It was time to suck it up! *If they do come, they must not see that I've cried*, he thought. The pictures drawn with sweat in the coal dust on the many miners' faces told him that there would be no denying where his lines would have come from.

When they were on the farm, his family wondered, quite often, where the next meal would come from. Thinking that you're going to die makes you believe that not getting regular meals is a mere inconvenience.

He was in there for thirty-six hours before they got him out; two of his brothers were the first to get to him. If he had not been so young and so fit, not too many more hours and he *would* have died.

Forty-six years later

He stood 5'10" on his left leg; his right, he stood 5'8". To the little boy who was watching him pull his brand-new shoes out of the box, he stood larger than life.

He had a wistful look as he stared at the shoes that he turned over in his hands. They were brand-new orthopedic shoes that were designed especially for him. The right shoe was built up the two inches that his leg was lacking, with a very lightweight material. When he tried them on he stood up and danced a little jig for the little boy.

"Boy, that sure feels good!"

"Granddaddy, why is that shoe so ugly?"

"Ah, well you see, they had to make the shoe so ugly because I'm so pretty!"

"That's silly!" the little boy said with a cute little laugh.

"No, Kev . . . Your granddaddy has a short leg and they had to build up his shoe so that he could walk better," said the grandmother.

"Why couldn't he walk better?" asked the grandson.

"It got broken in a mining accident," replied the grandfather.

"Oh, I see!" said the little boy with wide eyes who thought that what his grandfather had said was a "minding accident," which made him think of all the times that he himself hadn't minded his mother and was dealt with in a fashionable, yet painfully corporal way. He believed that his grandfather's mother must have broken his leg, probably by accident, and thought that it would be best to say no more.

He took the little boy by the hand and went outside to walk about a while. His mind went back a million miles . . . and fifteen minutes ago.

***

Dan and his two older brothers were in the field plowing, hoeing, and planting when they heard the dinner bell practically being rung off its post. It was two o'clock in the afternoon; lunch had been over for an hour and a half. Unusually, their father sent them back into the field without him so that he could stay behind to rest.

"I think I better stay. I'm feeling a little sick . . . It's my stomach . . . I don't really understand. I've never been sick a day in my life," the father had proclaimed.

The three knew what that bell meant; someone at the house was in serious trouble so they took off running as fast as they could. They covered the quarter mile of furrowed ground furiously, kicking up huge amounts of dust and showering dirt in every direction. When they got to the porch, they bounded into the house to find their mother leaning frantically over their father who appeared to have fallen next to his bed.

"Mother! What happened?" Bill asked anxiously, trying to get his breath.

"I don't know! Get him some water!" their mother frantically demanded.

Dan flew out onto the back porch and brought back a ladle of water with half of it fleeing its nest. Their father managed to open his eyes. Without saying anything he shook his head, declining the water, grimacing in tremendous pain. Clutching his wife's arm, he passed from the insignificant little world that he had fought so hard to tame.

Mrs. Sanders and her eight children, who were still at home, stood around the lifeless body taking one last melancholy look before they would set about the task of getting him ready. There were no paramedics to be called to resuscitate him. There were no police to be called for an investigation. There was no coroner to call to determine the cause of death. This burden sat squarely on their shoulders. The four oldest sons gently took their father and placed him on his bed.

The ringing of the bell alerted the neighbors who all stopped what they were doing and hastily made their way to the Sanders' home. They all knew before they arrived that something serious had happened. Mrs. Sanders walked out and stoically gave the news.

"My dear Noah has gone to be with his Lord," she stated calmly.

"What happened to him?" asked one of the neighbors.

"I'm not really sure . . . He said that his stomach was bothering him. He thought the heat was too much, so he went to lie down and that's when I heard him hit the floor. He was in a lot of pain . . . Sweat was running off him—"

"Probably his heart," stated an elderly woman.

The rest nodded their heads in unison. All of them had family members who had died of a heart attack or stroke.

Mrs. Sanders went inside and told the children to leave the bedside and wait outside. Bill and Robert stayed behind to help undress their father and a couple of older ladies set about the task of cleaning him and re-dressing him. Being old pros, they wasted no breath; the work was done quickly.

Several of the men went to Noah's toolshed and gathered shovels and picks, and a couple of others hitched the wagon and rode into town to have his casket made. The undertaker, who was also the casket maker and the preacher, already knew Noah's size, just as he knew everyone's size in those parts.

"You'll be a size 7, Mr. Noah, I do believe," quipped the undertaker one afternoon when Noah was at the local mercantile store.

Noah wasn't intimidated by the fact that he was in the presence of a preacher; they had been drinking buddies and he had no qualms saying, "To hell with you, Creighton! I'll be the one having to build your casket. Think I'll build it outta iron so as you cain't get out when the Lord comes back!"

"Won't matter what you make it out of. The Lord *will* get me out. He'll bust my grave wide open! You, on the other hand—"

"Yeah well, when he sees that ugly mug of yours, he probably gonna push you right back in!"

"Uh-huh, and by the time he finds your grave, it'll be the third coming!"

"Daddy, I didn't think there was a third coming," said John innocently as he looked up at Noah.

"Shush that talk, son. Me and Preach is just havin' some fun."

"But, Daddy, Mama says you'll go to hell if you make fun of the Lord."

Noah looked at the preacher, smiling cynically while smacking John on the back of the head.

"Well, John, I don't reckon you needs to tell yor mama do you, that yor daddy is going to hell, and don't forget to mention our preacher, who'll be going right along wi' me?" Noah said with a robust laugh.

Creighton smiled his piano keyboard smile and said, "Looks like your son is more concerned with our souls than we are! Don't worry, son. The Lord does forgive such foolishness."

***

Dan walked with the others up the road the mile and a half to the cemetery. Once they got to the family plot, one of the men who was facing away from the sun looked at his shadow to determine which way was east and traced out the lines to mark Noah's grave in the feckless soil.

"Joe, are you sure that's east?"

"Reckon it'd have to be . . . Sun's to my back, ain't it?"

"Well, jus' 'cause it's to yer back don't mean yer facin' due east!"

"There ain't but one east! Sun's to my back. It's past noon an' it's gonna set in the west and that's where east is an' that's where Noah's feet is gonna be!" said Joe as he pointed.

"All right then, but ain't ye ever noticed all these folks' feet in this here cemetery is a pointin' ever which way?"

"Jus' ferget it an' let's get to it afore poor ol' Noah starts a stinkin'. Oh, I is sorry Master Dan!" said Mr. Thorndike, who was a deacon of the church.

Dan nodded his forgiveness and looked down pensively and said, "Pops was a character. He's probably lookin' down havin' a grand time watchin' y'all."

After digging down a couple of feet, the gravediggers stepped out of the hole and handed Dan a shovel. They were afraid that if they didn't start the hole for him that his state of mind might cause him to lose concentration and dig willy-nilly.

"Thank y'all," he said while thinking, *Reckon it's time for me to be a man now. Daddy, you told me I was soft . . . Maybe so, but I won't be no more.* He looked in the direction of the house and said aloud, "I'm not gonna be soft no more."

He was only six days from fifteen and he had never been soft. Even though his father was a good-natured man, he had been very hard on all his boys. However, he wasn't hard on his wife; she was hard on him. Noah worked hard, he drank hard, he laughed hard, and he made love hard. Dan had never had a moment to be soft. Noah knew that. It's just the way it was.

Bill, Robert, and John made their way to the cemetery. Bill jumped into the two-thirds finished grave to help his brother. Robert followed shortly and nodded to Dan that he would take over for him.

Dan patted Robert on the shoulder and climbed out and saw tears welling in John's eyes, who was trying to hide them.

"It's all right, little brother," Dan said softly. "To everything there is a season, and a time to every purpose under the heaven . . ."

"A time to be born, and a time to die; a time to plant, and a time to pluck up that which is planted," Mr. Thorndike continued the verse. "A time to weep, and a time to laugh; a time to mourn, and a time to dance . . ."

After the grave was finished, Mr. Thorndike gave his own account of his understanding.

"You young fellows know . . . I know this might not sound right, but tomorrow we're gonna plant y'all's daddy, but that don't mean he's gonna stay down here," he said while pointing at the grave. "He was a righteous man and y'all know that Jesus'll come back to pluck him out of that grave and all the righteous along with him. So y'all take a look . . . All of you . . . That grave looks the same now as it will when that happens, except old Noah going to be standing right here, right where we are! So take heart."

"Man! Everybody better watch their step 'cause there sure is gonna be lots of holes!" said one of the not-so-tactful neighbors as he surveyed his surroundings.

"Well, we better hope there's gonna be lots of holes! But you know what, Salmon, you might be stuck in yor grave for all eternity, what with comments like that, but if ya change ya stinkin' ways I believe there might even be hope for you!" replied Mr. Thorndike.

Everyone there knew Mr. Salmon very well and all had heard him snicker a time or two at church when the preacher was getting down and dirty, especially when he was preaching about fornication and adultery (and not the least bit funny with his sermon). Regardless, Mr. Salmon brought a semblance of a smile to the faces of everyone in the digging party.

It was close to dark when the small crew returned to the house. Mrs. Sanders was sitting in a chair, next to her husband's bed, softly caressing his weather-worn hands and face and singing, even more softly, his favorite hymn.

"Bill, you and Robert need to go on down to town and telegraph your uncle Willard that his brother has died. That makes three of 'em now I reckon. Willard's the only one to make fifty. The only one that had sense enough to leave these parts," Mrs. Sanders lamented as she looked up sadly at her boys. "Go get the money outta the jar. Probably be faster for you to just saddle up Esther and Ruth and ride them in."

"Yes, Mama," Bill said soberly.

Robert knew Willard's address, which was why he was going, but he sometimes had trouble talking. Bill was good with words but he couldn't find his way out of a room with one door. Neither was very good by himself, but they functioned well together.

When the boys got to the telegraph office and told the telegrapher about their father, the kind gentleman refused to take their money. He too had knocked down a few shots with Noah "back in the day" and was truly saddened by the news.

Uncle Willard received the news when he arrived home from work that evening. Because the weather was already hot, Willard knew that they would have to get Noah in the ground the next day. This fact was going to make it difficult for him to make the funeral.

Willard was the head foreman of the main coal mining company in Birmingham, and when he told his bosses of his brother's demise, they agreed to let him off work at four o'clock instead of six o'clock, the day of the funeral.

Willard got one of the men at the mine to cover for him because the train schedule from Birmingham to Tuscaloosa would force him to wait until seven o'clock to leave. So he left the grounds at three thirty still covered in coal dust; he barely got to the station in time to catch the four o'clock coal train. He knew the conductor and would get a ride in the caboose.

By the time he got to the cemetery the pallbearers were about to lower Noah into the ground. Of course the preacher, who always dragged every funeral on seemingly forever, talked a little longer when he saw Willard coming down the road. When the preacher was finished, Willard nodded thanks to him then stepped in and grabbed a shovel and handed it to the oldest son, Robert, who took one shovel full of dirt and gently dropped it on the casket. Robert then handed it to Bill; each son took their turn in order of their birth.

Willard took the shovel back from the youngest son and began to fill the grave himself while remembering all of the trouble that he and his brothers would seem to get into. Some of the neighbors grabbed the other shovels and helped.

Willard paused for a moment and looked over at his mother's tombstone and stated plainly for all to hear, "Mama, please do forgive your sons. I haven't no doubt we put you in that grave a little early. Maybe Noah here will explain it all to ya, I hope."

Most of the men who were standing there knew exactly what Willard was talking about, but nothing in their look or body language gave them away so their wives and children were none the wiser.

Once the funeral party broke up and the Sanders returned to the house, they sat down to a modest supper that had been prepared by the same two ladies who had helped to prepare Noah.

"Lily, I know this is sudden, but have you thought about what you're going to do?" asked Willard.

"I've tried, Willard, but I don't know where to turn," replied Lily.

"To be plain, Lily, they are talking about hiring a lot of new men at the mining company. We're stepping up production 'cause there's talk of war in Europe. But they won't take anybody less than fifteen years old so we could hire your three oldest boys, if Dan has turned fifteen."

"He's fixin' to, in just a few more days."

The thought of getting off the farm excited Dan to no end, causing him to momentarily forget to chew. When he started to speak, he spewed potatoes onto the table.

"Dan! What on earth is the matter with you?" Lily fussed.

After a brief pause, Willard continued, "I know, at first, this will be hard, but the three of them can make more money in a week than anybody else here in these parts can make in two months."

This revelation caused the sap in Lily to rise and Dan to get even more excited, but the food went where it was supposed to this time. However, she was not used to change of this magnitude.

"I don't know, Willard, the boys have learned quite a bit. I believe they could take over the blacksmith shop and do okay."

"They could do 'okay,' Lily . . . With all of you working, you could eke out a living. You know how hard that's going to be, but if they go to the mine, none of the rest of you will have to work and that'll give you more time with your children."

"Let me think about it. I'm not sure I can leave Noah this soon," Lily lamented.

"Lily, Noah is not back there in that cemetery. That is just his body! Part of his spirit is with you now and it will be with you always, no matter where you go. He will be with you in Birmingham just the same as he is here."

"I'll have to sleep on it. Can I let you know in the morning?"

"Sure, but I'll have to get up in time to catch the five o'clock train. Will that give you enough time?"

"I get up by four o'clock anyway. I reckon I can get up an hour earlier. I'll get the boys to hitch the wagon in the morning and I'll drive you to the station. I'll let you know when you board the train and not a bit sooner! It won't change a thing if I do. Get some sleep!"

The next morning Lily drove Willard to the station. The only conversation they had on the fairly short ride was small talk. As promised, she let him know just as soon as his foot hit the first step.

"Willard, I reckon you convinced me. I'm going to have to sell my house. I don't know if that blacksmith shop is worth anything. How much time do ya suppose we have before they'll hire somebody else?"

"Lily, you won't have more than a few days. There'll be people waitin' in line. The boys can come stay with me until you get your house sold."

"No, Willard, your wife won't stand for that! If Providence decides that we are to move to Birmingham, then God will provide an answer."

Not surprisingly, that very afternoon, one of Noah's best friends, who was very opportunistic and also knew a lot about blacksmithing and farming (he always told him how to fix everything, which always ticked off Noah), came to the house and offered Mrs. Sanders a fair, but uninspiring sum. She was surprised at how quickly that God did move Noah's friend to act, but did not question His wisdom and took the money.

The bosses of the mining company reluctantly agreed to give the family two weeks to get into a new home. They were fond of Willard and knew that he would be hard to replace, which they would have had to do if they had not given in. As a matter of fact, when originally they were being obstinate, Willard placed his hat on his head and was headed out the door with the words that Culberson Mining Company (whom he never even talked to!) had offered him a better job with better pay.

Willard got his nephews hired and himself a raise to boot. He knew that he would have to drive the boys hard to keep from looking bad to his bosses. He wasn't too worried though. He knew that no matter how hard he drove them, it would not be any harder than what his brother and sister-in-law had always done.

***

"Hallelujah! Me and Bill ain't even going to have to go in the mine," stated Robert when they received their orders after they reported to the mining office.

"To hell with y'all," said Dan. "I'm going in the mine and what's more I don't mind goin' in the mine!"

"You won't, will ya? Well, when you come out, you gonna look black as ol' Uncle Tom!" Bill retorted.

"Yeah well! I'm gonna make a dollar a week more than y'all and that means I bet I can get the prettier girls!"

"You too little to do any girl much good!" Robert said zealously while pretending to go after Dan's crotch.

Dan jumped back and swung wildly at Robert's head without really trying to hit him. Dan had never had a girlfriend and really didn't know what to do with one anyway. Besides, fifteen-year-olds weren't allowed in the company of girls by themselves.

"You ain't gonna get to keep that dollar anyway, so I believe the sanctity of womanhood is safe for the time being from ol' Dan Sanders!" chimed in Bill.

"Bill, what's sanctity mean?" Robert asked.

"Ain't sure, Robert, just heard somebody say it once."

"Blast it, you two is a couple a knuckleheads!" Dan shot back.

***

It was the second day of the sixth week of work, very much the same as any other day. As usual their mother stood at the doorway handing each of them their lunch pails, which was the extent of her affection. Mrs. Sanders was an Irish immigrant whose parents died on the boat over. She was raised by her uncle who had fought in the Civil War as a cavalryman alongside Nathan Forrest. They said that he was so tough that he ate nails for breakfast. Good or not, she assimilated much of his personality as her own.

As Dan took his lunch pail, he looked his mother in the eye, which, to his surprise, chilled him to the bone. They gave each other a nod and a very slight smile. Very concerned, Dan looked back at his mother as he walked out to the street and saw that she was wiping her brow.

When the trio got out of earshot Dan said, "Somethin' seemed wrong with Mama. I never seen her look scared before. She's never looked me in the eye so long either. Felt like she was trying to tell me something."

"Naw, stop worryin'. She probably was wonderin' how you got so ugly while the rest of us is so pretty!" chided Bill.

"I didn't see nothin'. She could be just going through the change that women go through," said Robert.

Dan had no idea what Robert was talking about. It wasn't that he was ignorant of the birds and the bees; he had seen plenty of farm animals copulating. Menopause, on the other hand, was a foreign subject that most people didn't talk about. It was just always called "the change."

The fact is that Mrs. Sanders had a dream the night before that Dan was calling out to her. In the dream she had run to a spot of ground and could hear him calling from under her feet. She had also dreamt of her husband's fatal heart attack the night before and was worried that this dream was also going to come true. She paced about the house for at least ten minutes, then scolded herself for being such a sissy.

***

Several hours into the shift Dan was hard at it, but all during this time, he would imagine his mother's look. One of the other miners noticed that Dan was off into his own little world and reamed him out.

"Hey you! You think you're getting paid for starin'? Where's your mind at? Get back to work or I'll kick your ass!"

"Yes, sir. I apologize, it won't happen again."

"Well, see that it don't! There's a hundred people that I guarantee that wants your job."

Dan set back to work with great fervor and did not see the miner's smirk. One thing is for sure—Dan never daydreamed in that mine again.

It was time for lunch and everyone put down their tools to gather their pails. Dan had placed his in a recess to keep it out of the way and was racing to get it when a rumble began.

"Get out!"

Dan turned around in a panic and started to run toward the exit but a massive amount of stone and coal came down in front of him! He had nowhere to go but back to try to get under something, but it was too late; he was trapped!

Most of the miners made their way out of the tunnel very quickly as it collapsed. Unfortunately several didn't make it at all and were killed. Dan was lucky because another stone the size of a cedar chest just missed him by a couple of feet.

***

The lantern was painfully brighter than the sun to his unaccustomed eyes. The real pain came when they lifted the boulder from his leg, causing it to move ever so slightly. Then they had to roll him over onto a small stretcher, which nearly made him pass out. To make matters worse, since there was no room to stand erect, two men had to grab the handles at the same end to drag him to safety.

"Bill?"

"No, Dan, it's Robert. Bill's right over there," Robert said as he pointed.

"Well, Robert, I don't reckon it matters," Dan said with a weakened voice. "Where's Mama?"

"She was outside, Dan, but she had to go home. Somebody's gone to fetch her. She'll be here soon enough."

"Why did she go home? Couldn't Merrill stay with the little ones? How long was I stuck in here? It couldn't have been too long!" he stated deliriously, having forgotten everything that had happened to him.

"Dan, you was in here thirty-six hours!" Robert said to the sound of light laughter.

"All right! Ain't you Sad Sallys ready to git a move on? We gotta git this boy outta here! Let's git him to the infirmary," shouted Willard. "As for these other poor souls, a couple of you go on ahead and try to let their folks down as easy as you can."

When they finally got him out of the shaft, everyone who had waited on the outside gave a collective sigh of relief that at least one of them made it out alive. Muffled sobs could be heard moving through the ranks as the unfortunates were given the news of their husbands, fathers, and friends.

Mrs. Sanders had already returned along with the rest of Dan's siblings. She asked him if he was okay, and with his head raised slightly and as large a smile as a half-dead boy could muster, he replied with a bunch of gibberish.

"Mama, why's Dan's face look like he's been in a fire?" asked one of the younger siblings.

"'Cause this young fellow been ta hail 'n back!" answered another miner who held a canteen of water to Dan's mouth.

Dan managed to down quite a bit even though most of it went all over his chin and neck. He had held his "water" for the duration of his ordeal, but this newly acquired hydration kickstarted his kidneys and he was powerless not to let go. He was in no state to give a damn anyway!

Robert and Bill carried Dan into the infirmary that was at least a hundred yards from the tunnel. The two brothers were flabbergasted that a doctor had not already been summoned. They were also angered, but not surprised, that none of the owners had ever shown up.

Robert sent the youngest brother, Gabriel, into town to get the doctor who was found eating his supper and was in no hurry to finish.

"Is he bleeding, son?" asked the doctor while he was still slovenly masticating his very large mouthful.

"No, sir, I didn't see no blood."

"Is his neck broke?"

"No, sir, it's his leg."

"His leg? What's wrong with it?"

"I don't know, sir."

"All right, you run back down there and tell them I'll be there as soon as I can. Now don't you worry. Yor brother is gonna be fine."

Yes, Dan would be fine; except his leg wouldn't. By the time the doctor got there—which was as soon as he could two hours later—Dan's leg had already begun to set.

The doctor cut Dan's pants leg off and could see where the bone was bulging. He could tell that his knee had slipped a couple of inches upward. When he tried to pull on his leg, it wouldn't move. Dan let out a yell and told the doctor, in very colorful language, what he was going to do to him when he got up and about. (Later this created a joke inside the mining community, which was "don't ever pull Dan Sanders's leg or he'll ram a piece of coal up your ass!")

The doctor smiled slightly and told them there was not much that he could do except to immobilize the leg. He put a splint on it and sent him home.

***

19

Dan had to take up an entire bed by himself, but the little ones didn't care. They were actually quite happy to be able to help their big brother. In a few days the owners of the mine loaned the family a cot, which was a relief.

It was quite a while before the bone mended due to it being offset as much as it was. However, it did help that he was only fifteen and that some of the miners' wives brought him plenty of broth.

One wife insisted on giving him "bone knit" tea, which might have helped. One thing for certain was that it got his kidneys working overtime. They kept a Mason jar next to the cot, which was in easy reach of Dan. He kept filling it up and poor John wore out a path emptying it.

Once everyone was satisfied that Dan could get out of bed and use crutches, he did. The house was so small that he kept accidentally whacking the little ones with them. They just couldn't stay out of his way.

It was decided that Dan would go to live with Uncle Willard, who had plenty of room and had convinced his wife that it wouldn't hurt her to show a little charity and give Dan time to heal until he was able to get around without crutches and could go back to earning a living.

In less time than anyone expected, Dan threw down the crutches and started walking unaided. Before the accident Dan was very athletic and could run like the wind. Sadly, his normal running days were over. When he tried to run, his stride was so bizarre; it resembled an egg rolling end over end down a plank.

Often, during his daily exercise, he would stand out in the middle of the road with a dozen or so children around him and show them how comical it was to run around in a right-handed circle. Then, when he ran the opposite way he would fall down, making the children howl!

All of this activity eventually began to bother his hip and back. One day his younger brother John, who was visiting him, saw how much trouble he was having and ran to their uncle's wood shop and brought back a block of wood that he suggested to Dan to carve into the shape of the sole and nail it to the bottom of his shoe.

Dan thought, why not? So that is exactly what he did. It worked fairly well for standing, but it didn't work so well for walking, but it was still better than warping his spine. However, since he left it flat, his foot could not roll naturally, so he couldn't push off with it at all, but instead he had to exaggeratedly lift his leg or turn his foot at an extreme angle.

He went back to the drawing board and took a rasp and went to work putting a curve on his sole. He started looking at his shoe and realized that, for his foot to roll properly, he would need to round off the back of the heel too.

Once he got his shoe done, he put it on and walked inside to show his aunt. She was not amused! The sound of a wooden shoe clomping on a wooden floor was extremely loud, but the scratches in her finely finished floor really set her off.

Dan was a little dejected and so was brother John. They decided that they should just go outside and see how well he could manage. It was still a little strange because it was more obvious that one knee was two inches higher than the other.

***

Dan and John were sitting on the steps of the front porch waiting for Uncle Willard when he came home. Dan jumped up from the steps and ran toward him showing him how excited he was to have a halfway normal gait. Uncle Willard was quite impressed and patted Dan on the back.

"It was John's idea! Pops always said that John was the smart one."

"Yeah, it was my idea. But Dan's smart too. He's the one that made it. He can make anything . . . But Aunt Louise got mad 'cause Dan was making too much noise in the house and he scratched the floor too," said John.

"Well, looks like we're going to have to do something about that," said Uncle Willard. "What about we put a piece of leather on the bottom of that shoe?"

Dan and John slapped themselves on their foreheads in unison. "Why didn't we think of that?"

So they set about rasping the wooden sole down a little bit. When they finished rasping, they glued the piece of leather on with hot mucilage, then drove tacks in around the edges, recessing them far enough to keep them from scratching Aunt Louise's floors.

Very early the next morning, before daybreak, Aunt Louise got the boys out of bed and made them put on their clothes and instructed them to come downstairs in just their stocking feet. Dan and John looked at each other and shrugged. Why couldn't we put on our shoes? they thought.

They were puzzled at the sight of two pans placed on the floor next to each other. One was half filled with water; the other was partially filled with a very fine emery dust.

"Dan . . . John, here is each of you a rag . . . What you're going to do is get down on your hands and knees and dip the rag into the pan of water and then you're going to dip it in the emery and then you're going to rub out those scratches."

Dan just knew this was going to hurt his leg, but he knew better than to talk back to his aunt. He had seen more than one teenager whacked with a piece of stove wood. Being whacked with a piece of stove wood would be considerably more painful than his bum leg.

Getting down on the floor was more awkward than it was painful and Dan realized that he could adapt. So they set about the task at hand. They didn't want to do this all day so they worked at a furious pace. Their hands were moving so fast that they almost resembled the wings of a hummingbird.

***

Aunt Louise inspected their work and declared them finished and announced that breakfast was ready. They had been up for three hours, yet it was only seven o'clock. Louise stated that if they had taken any longer they would have had to skip breakfast since it was already getting so close to lunchtime.

The two boys ate their breakfast as though it was the first time they'd eaten in two weeks. As frenetically as they were devouring their eggs and ham and grits and rye bread and two glasses of milk each, it would seem impossible that all of it made it into their mouths.

Nothing was left on their plates and nothing fell on the floor or the table, much to the chagrin of Louise's pet terrier.

They were eager to get outside and horse around and were surprised that their request to be excused was denied.

"No, young masters, you are not finished," stated Aunt Louise in a matter-of-fact businesslike tone.

Dan and John looked at each other with the exaggerated expressions of wide-eyed fear. She had said that they were finished. What in the world were they to do next?

"The next thing we do is we have to re-stain and re-oil the floors."

Aunt Louise had said "we do," but the two boys knew that auntie meant that her role would be strictly supervisory and that they would be doing the "doing."

They got to work and did a pretty good job. They only had to redo two or three spots. Auntie was actually surprised at how well they did and saw that they had talent.

The main purpose of this exercise to Aunt Louise was to see if Dan was ready to go back to work. She knew that if he could spend five or six hours on his hands and knees and not give out quickly, he could be gainfully employed.

That night when Willard got home Louise announced that Dan was ready to go back to work. Willard stated plaintively that it would be cruel to put Dan back in the mine.

"He doesn't have to go back in the mine. Surely there are other jobs that he could do. You're the foreman. You can find him something!" Louise demanded.

"I suppose I could. One of our wagon drivers was shot the other night coming out of a brothel," Willard said disgustedly. "The doc says it'll be a week or two before he can come back to work. I'll take Dan with me in the morning. I know Dan was good with horse-drawn wagons, but what we got is mules and those darn mules is pretty stubborn," said Willard with a sigh.

The next morning Dan went with Willard and John went back home. Dan was not particularly excited to go anywhere near the mine, but what choice did he have? Everyone had to earn their keep.

You didn't have a psychiatrist to help deal with your problems; there was no one to feel sorry for you either. *Just work!*

When they got to the mine, Willard went to get the okay for Dan to work. Dan walked over to the tunnel that had collapsed on him and went in a few feet. He could see that it had been cleared and shored up, but he still felt uneasy standing inside.

When the memory of his hallucinations returned, he began to laugh out loud, which of course echoed through the chambers for all of the miners to hear. Several of them who were close enough looked back at the silhouette of a perceived crazy person and hollered at him, "What's so funny? Who the hell is that?" yelled one of the miners.

"It's me . . . It's Dan. I'm the one that damn rock fell on!"

"What the hell are you doing back here? Looks like you'd have better sense," yelled another.

"Just thought I'd look in. I ain't goin' back in there! I think they're goin' to put me on a wagon. At least I hope so," replied Dan.

"That damn mule team they'll give you ain't no better than coming back here in this mine! They liable to kick you in the head and leave you layin' there. Only good thing about it is you will be in the sunshine . . . All right then, good luck to ya," one of them declared as they all turned to walk stoopedly deeper into the mine.

Dan got his mule team, which was pretty stubborn, but he was twice as stubborn and figured that if he couldn't outsmart a couple of mules, then he didn't deserve to be in the human race. Regardless of what the miners said, he was quite happy to be on the outside and dealing with a couple of ornery mules.

***

Into the Dawn

Dan was seventeen now, and after the eighteen months he had with his team, he couldn't understand the complaints he heard; they were just mules. They always seemed to know where they were going. This team was so reliable in fact that Dan was quite often able to take a nap while they made their way back to the mine. The slow, methodical pace; the steady clip-clop of their hooves; and the slight shaking of the wagon would sometimes put Dan under in minutes.

He was dreaming of some faraway place; he was looking through a window while riding in a Pullman railroad car at some beautiful snowcapped mountains. As the train rounded, a curve, the glint of sunshine that was coming from behind the mountains caused him to squint. As he put his hand over his eyes, the train began to violently bump along and was about to derail!

When he was jarred awake, he discovered that one of his mules had thrown a shoe at approximately the same time that they had hit a rough patch in the road. Dan pulled back on the reins, locked the break, and got off to take a look. He thought about walking back to see if he could find the shoe, but decided to hell with it!

Each wagon was equipped with a hammer, nails, and extra shoes for such occasions. Dan had seen many horses shoed by his father, but he had never done it. He was several miles away from the mine and did not want to return with a mule with an uneven gait that resembled his own, so he decided to re-shoe the animal himself.

As he was driving in the nails, he saw a wagon coming that was being driven by a father with two teenage daughters on board. He had been getting the itch for a girlfriend and this little detail sort of distracted him.

Dan kept looking up and he hammered his finger, but determinedly he didn't flinch. And just before the wagon got even with him, he drove a nail in too far, which caused the mule to kick him right out in front of the oncoming wagon!

The horses of the oncoming wagon calmly stopped right before stepping on him, as though they were used to having young men flung out in front of them every day.

"Are you all right, young man?" asked the father.

"I'm fine," wheezed Dan.

The two teenage girls giggled while hiding their mouths with their hands. The father shshed them, but that only made it worse. The giggles turned into outright laughs.

Dan was a little more than embarrassed, but one of the girls caught his eye. His gaze stopped her giggling as their eyes locked. He was in love! *This is the girl I'm going to marry!* he thought.

Dan stood up and dusted himself off and grinned but forgot to introduce himself. The father knew what Dan was looking at, and to keep him from getting his hopes up, he told him that they were there from Hamburg, Georgia, visiting his brother and would return home very soon. Dan had never been instructed in the social graces and nodded his head.

"Well, son, if you're all right, we'll be getting on. I need to get my brother's wagon back to him before dark. Good day . . . Be careful with that mule," the father said while looking askance.

"Yes, sir, I'll definitely watch what I'm doing next time."

Off they drove while Dan watched helplessly while the girl he was going to marry turned back to look as she gave a discreet little wave.

That would be the last time that Dan ever hesitated for the rest of his life. He felt that he had just missed an opportunity, and based on his brief life, he knew that real opportunities rarely presented themselves.

He couldn't get that girl out of his mind for some time, but eventually he did begin to think of other things and other girls. Other girls enjoyed getting his attention, but he never felt like being serious with any of them. He was a little shy about his leg and his clompy shoe and sometimes wondered if the girls that did pay attention to him were just feeling sorry for him.

After a few years of driving the mule team, one of the mules became lame and was sent to the slaughterhouse. It was the mule that had kicked him into the road and he wondered sometimes if that mule might have kicked him toward his destiny if he had not stumbled his chance so badly.

The war was winding down, and rumors were swirling about that the mine would start firing people as soon as it was over. He decided that it was time to quit before he was fired and go find a better job. He was presented an "opportunity" in 1919 to go to Hamburg to take truckloads of black men down to Florida to pick oranges. He was hoping that he might run into the girl that was in that wagon if he took the job. This chance was as much the motivation for his decision as anything.

***

When it was time to load up all the workers were mildly excited about their pending prosperity and were eager to get rolling; they had bought the bullshit that they were going to make $3 a day. Dan greeted them all with a nod and a smile, which was unusual, and they all gave a big smile in return. The business owner was a little miffed and took Dan aside.

"Look, young man, it's best you didn't get too friendly with these n——rs. People don't like the looks of it!"

"Mr. Sims, there ain't a soul out here this early to see it. I'm driving these men nearly four hundred miles, and I'd hope if I was friendly enough, none of 'em'll cut my throat and steal your truck," Dan lied. His best friend and his family were black. Dirt-poor starving people who helped each other out had no color to him.

On the first night when Dan pulled the truck off the road and everyone settled around a little campfire that was used to cook their food, one of the men dared to ask Dan a question.

"Sir, what might your name be?"

All the other men looked shocked at this little man's attempt at etiquette. Dan smiled knowing the testicles that this simple question took.

"Why, sir, my name is Dan. As a matter of fact my whole name is Daniel George Sanders. You can call me Dan . . . And what might your name be, sir?"

There's no way in hell that a white man was so cordial to a black man! Most of them figured that since Dan was outnumbered and there were no other white people around, he was pretending to be nice. But Dan's smile, the one that so many people would remember at his funeral many years later, allayed their fears and everyone relaxed.

"Why, Mr. Dan, sir, my name is Raymond Harley Everett. But ever'body calls me Coconut."

"So, Raymond, why in the world do they call you Coconut?"

"Well, the plain truth is it's because of my head."

"What about your head?"

"It's hard . . . as hard as a coconut. That's what they says. It might be 'cause I'm stubborn, or it might be 'cause one time I fell off a scaffolding and cracked my head on the concrete but I got up and kept on a working."

"Sounds to me like it's because of both," Dan replied while taking an instant liking to this little big man.

The trip was arduous to Florida due to the distance and the heat and the bumpy dirt roads. The truck could hardly go fast enough to outrun the mosquitoes, which at times were quite fierce. Dan tried weaving back and forth to kick up as much dust as he could, but all that did was choke the men in the back. The only other thing to do was to close the flap on the back of the cover, which made the heat even more unbearable.

When they arrived at the plantation (which was exactly what it was), the men all bailed out of the back and waited for the foreman to arrive.

Dan saw a man on horseback coming toward them at a near gallop, kicking up a cloud of dust. When he got close enough, everyone could see that he was armed with a sidearm, a whip, and a shotgun that was holstered on the saddle.

He was a despicably ill-mannered, burly-looking son of a bitch who made no bones about what their fate was. These black men were still seen as no better than animals, especially to the rich and the people that worked for them. They all knew immediately that they had been had.

"You n——s are gonna do a job and you're gonna work from sunup till sundown. You're gonna eat your lunch in fifteen minutes if you've worked hard enough to earn your lunch! You're gonna get water every four hours, that is if you work hard enough. If you slouch, you ain't getting shit. If I catch any of you partaking in the oranges, I'm gonna shoot your ass and leave you dead on the spot. If any of you try to leave before the picking is finished, I'll shoot your ass and leave you on the spot. We got fifteen armed men around here to see that everything is done right. You'll get Sundays off and that's when you'll get to go down to the creek to bathe. Now, if you got any questions, you better keep them to yourselves 'cause we don't like n——s to ask questions."

Dan wondered, *If there are fifteen guards, why the hell don't they pick the goddamn oranges themselves! They could just shoot the branches and pick them up off the ground!*

The man looked at Dan and attempted an unconvincing smile and told him everything was going to be all right, just go on back to Georgia and bring on down another load.

Dan's blood pressure went sky high. Didn't this ass know that the Civil War was over? Dan related to these offspring of slaves because his grandmother Sanders came to America as an indentured servant and he grew up with that unpleasant stigma hanging over his head.

***

Dan headed back to Georgia, but not to get another load of black men. He was going to take the truck back to the owner and quit and was going to warn every black man he saw not to go to Florida to pick oranges.

Dan only stopped to get gas when he could find it. He drove straight back and did not sleep and was exhausted by the time he returned to Hamburg.

When he got to downtown on the main street, he was shocked to see one of the black men, who was very short, that he had carried to Florida. It was Coconut! He couldn't believe his eyes so he went over to him to ask if, indeed, he was the one that he had driven to Florida. The little fellow told him with a huge grin, "Yes, sir, and I ain't goin' back, no way! I ain't never seed such a bad man in my life as that!"

"Coconut! How in hell did you get away and make it back so fast?"

"Mr. Dan, bein' as little as I am, I don't think nobody ever saw me! When they was showin' us to the bunkhouse, I just eased out a line and walked on down the road 'til I found a freight train headin' north. Had no idea where it was goin', but lo and behold, it came back here to Hamburg!"

"Well, Coconut! I reckon that train was a heck of a lot faster than that truck!"

"Yes, sir, Mr. Dan, and I'm glad it was!"

"Well, good luck to you, Raymond Harley Everett."

"Coconut, if you don't mind, sir. I can't believes you remembered my whole name."

"Me neither, Coconut. I'm not too good with names usually. See you around perhaps."

"Don't say that too loud, sir! Don't wants people thinking you loves a nigger."

Suddenly Dan had a very sad look and shook the little man's hand good-bye and didn't care who saw.

Dan telegraphed his mother and told her that he was going to return to Birmingham. He told her of the immorality of what he had just done and that he refused to take the money when Mr. Sims tried to hand it to him. He told her that he would be back within a week and not sooner because he wanted to look around Hamburg a little while.

What he wanted to look around for was that girl. Since he didn't know her name, he knew that the odds were greatly against him. He hung out on the streets and walked around in the neighborhoods, but what he didn't know was that she lived seven or eight miles away in a little cabin in the woods.

One Sunday at breakfast time, Dan went into the local diner and ran into an acquaintance that he had met a few days earlier. His name was Herbert Watson.

"So, Dan, what is it that brings you to Hamburg in the first place?" Asked Herbert.

"To tell you the truth, I'm not really sure. I carried a load of workers to Florida and decided that I wouldn't do that anymore. It was hard for me to stand there and look at those men who could've been killed for really no reason. I saw the look of death in their eyes."

"You talking about a bunch of n——s? I don't get what you're so torn up about. They got to eat too. You was just doing them a favor."

"It didn't feel like a favor. It felt like I was turning my back on a fellow human being. I don't want to stand before God on Judgment Day and explain to Him how I could betray those men."

"Well, ya didn't really know 'til you got down there, did ya?"

"No, I didn't and that would be my only saving grace! I figured if I had said anything, that man on that horse wouldn't have thought twice about shootin' me and those black men would still be down there anyway. So I kept my mouth shut and brought back the truck and told the fellow thanks, but no thanks."

"Yeah, sometimes it's best to keep ya mouth shut. Especially when you're talking about women!"

Dan looked sideways at Herbert, wondering how he got on the subject of women. But it shook his mind back to the purpose of coming to Hamburg in the first place.

"Speakin' of women, I've been looking for one since I've been here and I got no idea where to look."

"Ah hell! That's easy . . . You go on over to Peggy's and you'll have your choice of several…, some of 'em pretty good-lookin' too! I'll take you by there whenever you're ready to go. It'll cost you two dollars, but if ya ain't got that much to spare, then they'll do it by hand for $.50."

"Damn, Herbert! That ain't what I'm talking about! A few years ago, I saw this girl riding with her sister and her father on the road where one of my mules threw a shoe, and when I was tryin' to shod him, he kicked me right out in front of 'em. As she was getting away, I told myself that I was going to marry her."

"That sounds a little crazy! That mule kick you in the head?"

Dan gave a disgusted look and no reply.

"So why come to Hamburg?"

"'Cause that's where they said they were from!"

"Well, what was her name?"

"I didn't get her name and I didn't get her father's name neither! All I got was that they was visiting her father's brother there in Birmingham."

"That ain't really a lot to go on, now is it?"

"Nah, ain't a lot at all. All I know is that she was a real jewel, an angel."

"What you gonna do about it?"

"Cain't say, really."

"It's going to take a hell of a lot of luck for you to find her. I'd say ya might as well go on back to Birmingham. Who knows? She might go visit her uncle and you might just run into her back home."

Dan let out a little snicker and shook his head and took a sip of coffee. He figured he'd just give up. He might not have given up in the mine, but that was life or death. Love might seem like life or death sometimes, but it really isn't and he knew it's best to give up sometimes.

Dan kept replaying the look that that girl had given him, which he had never gotten from any other girl. Maybe, he thought, it was him. Maybe he had not given any other girl the chance to look at him that way. He would start over tomorrow, but today he was going to go down to the creek.

"Say, Herbert, what say we go down to Johnson's Creek and wade around a bit? Maybe even go fishin' . . . You got any fishin' poles?" prodded Dan.

"Yeah, of course I got some poles and I got a canoe. It's a pretty good-size one, but me an' you can still handle it all right."

"That sounds like a pretty good idea . . . Ya got any rum?"

"Rum! Of course I do an' got most anything else you can think of too."

"Sounds like we're in for a good time! Ya know, Herbert, I've never been drunk in my life so I reckon now is as good a time as any."

"Naw . . . Naw! If you ain't never been drunk then it's best you didn't get that way in that canoe! It's hard as hell for a drunk man to swim, especially in water that's as swift as that creek. We'll get on downstream and find a good place to get out and then you can get drunk, but not afore."

"I cain't swim no way! So I reckon it's best I didn't fall out of that damn canoe anyway."

Herbert lived close to the river so he and Dan had to walk down to the riverbank to fetch the canoe. They held the canoe over their heads as they carried it back to the house to load it on Herbert's truck. Because of Dan's bouncy stride, it kept hitting Herbert on the head.

"Dan! Why the hell do you keep bouncing this damn canoe?"

Dan was wearing regular shoes by this time and said, "Herbert, ain't ya ever seen my leg? My right one is two inches too short. I got caught in a cave-in in a coal mine an' a big ol' rock came crashing down on it. I think my brother told them to leave me in there," Dan said jokingly, "but I reckon somebody got to feelin' guilty an' they finally got me out! My leg already started settin' by the time they got to me. It don't really bother me that much."

"Well, right now it sure as hell bothers me!"

"Keep ya pants on! Were not more than thirty feet away."

***

Into the Light

As the two young friends headed toward Johnson's Creek, Dan began to dread his journey home in the coming days. He didn't know for sure if he could find any work, but he did know that he was not going back in that mine.

During the last couple of years, he had learned some skills in carpentry at the mine site by helping to build several new buildings. He had helped with the framing, the roofing, a good deal of mortar work and concrete laying.

He knew there had to be something or someone in Birmingham who might use his skills. He barely spoke to Herbert on the way to the creek because of his concerns. He had completely forgotten about the girl.

They got to the creek right around ten o'clock and found a suitable place to launch. Once they loaded their fishing poles, bait, and of course the spirit-raising beverage, they were ready to shove off.

Herbert was amazed at how adept Dan was at paddling the canoe. Dan could paddle by himself without alternating sides and he could steer the same way. He learned the skill paddling small boats and canoes on the Black Warrior River.

"Say, Dan, how do you paddle like that? Reckon you could show me?"

"Sure . . . See you do it like this, you kinda twist your paddle a little bit under the canoe."

Herbert tried it but he couldn't do it. Dan tried showing him again and Herbert failed again, causing Dan to have to straighten out the canoe before they completely turned around. Herbert got frustrated and quit to let Dan do the paddling by himself.

Dan laughed and took a swig of the rum out of the little brown jug. He handed it to Herbert who did likewise, and of course, they kept handing it back and forth until they were feeling pretty good.

"So, Dan, what was it like bein' in that mine for so long?"

"Hebert, it weren't worth a damn! Ever'thing was goin' along just like always and there was a little rumble and somebody yelled and boom! Couldn't go no-where. Pretty big rock got on my leg an' broke it."

"Boy! I bet that had to hurt!"

"You ain't lyin'! Strangest thing about all of it though was—now remember it was pitch black in there an' I couldn't see my hand in front of my face—was I started seein' all of these shapes," Dan said as he drew all types of spirals and zig-zags with his fingers in the air.

"You know I knew a ol' Indian that lived in the desert an' they'd stuck him in a cave after they gave him some kinda stuff an' he said he saw all kinda strange things after he'd been in there a couple a days. He saw buffaloes an' horses an' stuff. I talked to a minister 'bout it an' he called all those shapes religious geometry. He showed me a book an' I took it to that ol' Indian an' he nearly cried when he seen those pictures! "

"Yeah, I saw my father an' he told me not to give up . . . told me my brothers was real close to gettin' me out . . . You know, Herbert, I felt as alone as I ever have been in my life an' I was real close to not believin' in God 'til that happened," Dan said pensively.

"Yep, you might say you was in a real dark place in your life!" Herbert mocked.

Dan took the paddle out of the water to feign hitting Herbert on the head, which caused the rummed up pair to give up a hardy chortle!

***

Within fifteen or twenty minutes, they reached the spot where Herbert knew was good fishing. They paddled the canoe right onto the narrow shoreline and staggered about while pulling the canoe out of the water. Both of them fell down, due to the influence of the rum and the accelerated effect of their exertion, causing them to laugh hard.

They got the fishing poles and the rum out of the canoe and began baiting their hooks. Herbert found a shady spot for the rum after taking another swig and then went straight to fishing. Dan's bait fell off his hook, but he didn't give a damn and cast it into the water anyway. He didn't really want to catch a fish to start with.

The two of them were talking loud enough to wake the dead, which slightly agitated the fish. Herbert didn't really care whether or not he caught a fish either. It's the fact that the men of that day always felt silly when they were just standing on a creek bank or in the water enjoying the sun and not actually doing anything.

"So, Herbert, what is it you do for a living?" Dan asked.

"I set tombstones."

"Yeah?"

"Yeah."

"Been doing it long?"

"Not too long . . . Just since I was twelve. I'm twenty-five now. How long is that?"

"That would be thirteen years I reckon, seems long to me . . . I'm twenty myself."

"Nah, time goes fast . . . I love the hell out of it!"

Dan contemplated that statement with a frown and continued to "fish".

"So, Dan, you want me to see if I can get you a job hauling marble?" Herbert asked after several minutes.

"Well, seeing as I don't have a truck of my own, I don't see how I could do that just yet."

"Oh, you wouldn't need a truck. All you'd be doing is going about three blocks down to the railroad yard and they'd load it for you onto a wagon most of the time and then sometimes onto a truck. Them mules haul more marble than that old truck any day."

"I don't know, Herbert. I've already told Mother that I'd be back home in a few days," Dan said as he put down his pole and walked over to the rum and took a swig.

"It was just a thought . . . I figured that Hamburg is a pretty far piece from those coal mines," said Herbert as he was pulling in a fish.

"Yep, it is that . . . I'll think about . . . Ugh, this rum and those grits I had this morning," Dan tried to say as he let out an uproariously unbridled belch.

Dan looked up at Herbert, wondering how in the hell such a masculine man could let out such an infinitely feminine little giggle! But Herbert had his head turned to see who was hiding in the bushes and in fact had not responded to Dan's belch at all.

It was at that moment that Dan reaffirmed his faith in God and the angels and destiny and happiness all in one, for the "giggle" came forward at Herbert's behest. It was in fact *the* girl!

Dan's heart was beating out of his chest and he had trouble looking at her. He kept his head down and his hands in his pockets. He started to sweat, especially under his arms, and he had another pocket of gas that was intensely fighting for its freedom, but Dan held tight. Even so, he would have found it impossible to speak at this moment.

"Dan, what's the matter? You act like you never seen a girl!" Herbert exclaimed as he went over to the girl to introduce himself. "Hi, my name's Herbert and this here's Dan. He ain't never seen a girl before so he don't know how to act. So what's yor name?"

From behind the bushes came another giggle. It was the girl's sister who had also been on the wagon when Dan was kicked into the road. It took a little extra prodding but she came out too.

"Dan, what's wrong? Why are you looking so stupid right now?" Herbert asked.

Dan kept pointing subtly at the girl, but was still having a hard time speaking. It took two or three stutters and a couple of throat clearings and the re-confinement of the up-and-coming belch before he could speak.

"It's . . . It's her. It's the girl I told you about. She's growed up a bit since last I saw her, but it's her just the same and that's her sister too," he said with a huge swallow.

"Now, miss, I don't mean to be impolite," said Herbert, "but I would actually like to know your name . . . And I'll bet you Dan over there wants to know it too, probably even more than I do."

"My name's Jewell," she said shyly, "and that's my sister Anna. She's a little bit older than me even though she don't look it."

"Hello, Jewell . . . my name's Dan. You probably don't remember but we met on a road near Birmingham," Dan said after finally finding his wits.

"We did? Are you sure?" Jewell asked innocently even though she did remember.

"Well . . . Why should you remember? It was a while back. You were visiting your uncle with your father and your sister—that is, if that is your sister. A mule kinda kicked me out into the road right in front of your wagon."

"Really? Maybe if I think about it a while I might remember, but it's just not shakin' out right now."

"Well . . . I reckon most any fool can be kicked out into the road by a mule," Dan said dejectedly.

"Any fool that'd be wearing a big old clompy shoe with a piece of wood nailed to the bottom of it!"

Dan looked down at his right foot with a frown because he could have sworn that he was wearing regular shoes and was shaken back into reality by this revelation. He suddenly began to grin and it was a most infectious grin.

"So you do remember! You had me goin' there. For a second I thought I had forgotten and put on that big ol' shoe! Then I remembered that I left it in Birmingham. In fact, I don't believe I've worn that shoe in at least a year! That's a good one!" he said as he busted out laughing.

"How could anyone forget such a handsome young man that got put right in my path—Ooo! I've got to go!" she exclaimed as she realized how forward she must have sounded. She took off running, with her hand covering her mouth, toward the house with her sister who was completely shocked at the behavior of her sister.

Dan now knew for certain that supernatural forces had to be at play; it was ordained that they be together. In his mind the reason that he had described her as a jewel was because the angels were trying to tell him her name. He just knew that he had caught lightning in a bottle and so did the darling Jewell!

Dan wanted to hang around until dark to see if Jewell would come back. Herbert wasn't too keen on the idea, and since it was his truck that brought them to the creek, he had the final say. He explained to Dan that the headlights on that truck were barely more than a couple of candles. Of course as slow as they had to drive that didn't really matter so much. No more traffic than there was they could have driven by starlight.

Dan was tempted to ask Herbert to leave him his canoe so he could sleep in it, but then realized he was losing his mind and would look like an idiot to the young girl anyway. So he grudgingly agreed to go home when it was time.

Once they were on the road Dan's mood changed for the better. He thought, *What the hell, if I marry her I'm going to be with her a very long time anyway, and who knows, she'll probably get tired of me before it's over with.*

"You know, Dan, if that girl is the right one and you get married, you're liable to be with her fifty or sixty years if you live long enough. If you want to drop me off at work tomorrow, you can borrow my truck and go on back to the creek."

"That'd be all right? I'd really appreciate it," Dan replied with a huge grin, being amazed that he and Herbert had the same thought.

"Of course it would be all right. I seen yor look . . . It was kinda stupid, kinda like that mule done kicked ya again, and the only way to straighten it out is for you to take yor tail on back down there and wade around until she shows up or you get tired of waiting."

"Yep, I think you're right . . . Heck, I might forget all about her by in the morning."

Herbert punched Dan on the shoulder and bellowed, "Bull shit, Dan! You ain't forgot about her in two years and all you did was see her in a bloomin' wagon and got one tiny little smile, I suspect, or maybe a little giggle and a little finger wiggle, if even that! So no! You ain't gonna forget her, not in one little bitty night!"

"Yep, I suspect you're right," Dan said while taking a really deep breath and letting out a really long sigh.

The next morning Dan got up at four o'clock after a restless night. He put on his shoes and paced back and forth in his hotel room for a half an hour, waking the customers, who were staying in the adjacent rooms.

Eventually the cook and the night manager knocked on his door and politely asked him if he could stop pacing or walk a little softer. Dan was pretty embarrassed by this revelation because he had no idea that he was making so much noise.

He softly apologized, and when the two informers left, he lay back down on the bed without taking off his shoes. He tried to bump his toes together to calm himself down, but he kept missing, well you know!

Well damn! he thought. *Wish I had my big old shoe . . . Hell, that sure is a silly thing to think! Don't know if I really do want to marry some girl if I'm going to be this damn silly . . . She sure is a cutie though . . . Oh Kentucky! What am I gonna do?*

When it was time, he went to see Herbert and borrowed his truck and the canoe. Normally the canoe was a little bulky for one person, but Dan's passions were running so high that it felt like a feather to him and he had no trouble getting it into the water. He shoved off and paddled with great intensity.

The sun wasn't very high yet, but already the day was looking bright and beautiful and was filled with promise. The weather was perfect. The water was perfect. The world was perfect.

He thought of nothing else but Jewell. His subconscious took over the paddling and the steering and the seeing. He didn't realize it, but he was about to pass the previous day's landing when he looked over and saw her sitting on a bucket next to an older lady breaking green beans into another bucket.

As he was floating past and looking back over his shoulder, he hit a log that was sticking out of the water. Pandemonium ensued as he began to flail about because, you may recall, he couldn't swim.

Jewell could. She could swim very well and she swam over to him. She grabbed hold of him and, strenuously swimming back to the creek bank, dragged him out of the water. The water wasn't really that deep. If he hadn't panicked, he could've stood up and gotten his head out and pretty much walked out, but Jewell couldn't. She was too short, but it didn't matter. She certainly was stout, which greatly impressed Dan.

There were a couple of times where he felt the bottom of the creek but he chose not to assist her. He was enjoying being held onto by such a cute girl without having to entice her to do so. Jewell's mother, on the other hand, was a little perturbed by the actions of such an incompetent boob such as Dan.

Jewell's mother walked toward the creek bank while looking at the heavens, asking God why such an idiot had to come by at such an inopportune time. Young men potentially drowning in her creek always put a damper on her plans.

"Jewell! Why not just let him drown? He should've been watching where he was goin' and on top of that it's not becoming for a young lady to expose herself the way you're doin' right now. Now go get in the house and get out of those clothes afore I tan yor hide!"

"Yes, Mama!" Jewell shouted as she ran back toward the house.

Dan watched her run off and was not disappointed at the sight of her wet clothes clinging to her very feminine form. He could see that she was very athletic looking and that was a definite positive because he figured on having lots of babies.

Don't think that Mama didn't see what he was looking at! His gaze was interrupted by a fierce swish and the sting of a small cane shaft against his neck! Before he could even react, his skin was already forming a ferocious welt.

"Ma'am! Why in the world did you do that?"

"You know good and well why I did that! You were lookin' inappropriately at my daughter and don't say you warn't neither. I saw you good and clear and I don't cotton to that one bit!"

"Yes, ma'am! I'm guilty as charged, but that is the girl I'm going to marry . . ."

"Oh, you is, is you? An' who says you is? It certainly ain't me!"

"I'm sorry, ma'am. I didn't mean to be so forward, but I haven't gotten her out of my mind for two years or maybe better."

"What do you mean? How do you know my daughter? I ain't never even seen you afore! Have you been hidin' out in the cattails?" she demanded angrily

"No, ma'am. It was near Birmingham a while back an' one of the mules that was pulling my wagon threw a shoe an' I wasn't paying any attention and that dang mule, pardon my language, ma'am, kicked me out onto the road in front of your husband's wagon and your daughter Jewell was with him."

"How come that mule to kick *you* jus' cause it threw a shoe?"

"Well, it was because I was tryin' to re-shoe the darn thing, and I drove a nail in too far and that blame mule didn't like it!"

"Maybe you shoulda had somebody wid ya that knew what he was a doin'!"

"Yes, ma'am, I guess I shoulda," Dan replied politely while trying not to get run off.

"So you want to court Jewell, does ye? Why not Anna? She's a year and a half older than Jewell . . . a little closer to your age, I'd say," the mother said while sizing up the potential husband. "She ain't had too many suitors, has that Anna, an' I mean to get her married first."

Dan could tell why too, but if he had said so he might get another whack on the neck by that cane pole. He was not ready to go back into Hamburg with matching welts.

"Well, ma'am, all I can tell you is that I got struck by lightnin' an' there ain't no other explanation."

Mrs. Smith knew that there was no arguing with being struck by lightning. She had been struck three times or at least that's how many marriages she'd had. (At least she knew that her husbands had been struck three times and one of them literally when he was plowing a field during a thunderstorm; he survived that, but not the falling off the roof.)

Suddenly Dan realized how much time had gone by and the canoe was probably going down stream so he excused himself of Mrs. Smith's company and hurried down the creek bank as far as he could until he saw the canoe. He was relieved to see that it was stuck in the rushes on the other side.

He felt confident enough to leave it where it was so he walked on back to renew his conversation with Mrs. Smith. Suddenly he realized that if that mine had not caved in on him he would have never met this pretty girl, which made him more determined than ever. He was going to ask Mrs. Smith if her husband might be at home or if he was in the fields or possibly at a job somewhere so that if need be he could come back at a later time to discuss the courtship of his daughter Jewell.

"Ma'am, I'm sorry to run off like that but I had to make sure that the canoe was okay . . . I'd like to introduce myself. My name is Dan Sanders. I'm from Birmingham and I was over here in Hamburg doing a small job for a fella that it turns out he wasn't such a good man as I thought and I quit. I know this is sudden like, but I really would like to court your daughter and I wonder if I might have a word with her father?"

"Well, I'm going to have to be frank with you . . . Her father is not going to listen to a word you say. I can take you to him, but I promise ye, he ain't going to hear ye. And by the way my name is Mrs. Smith."

"So he's available for me to see him at this time?"

"I guess I'd have to say that he is available at any time, but you ain't going to get to see him, 'less you got a shovel."

"I don't rightly understand. You can take me to him, but I cain't see him? Is that right?" Dan frowned with puzzlement.

"The fact is, son, Mr. Smith passed away about a year ago and he's, I guess you might say, a little under the weather these days or more as like under the dirt."

Dan wasn't sure if she was testing him or if she was just plain crazy. He felt uneasy about his quest for the hand of young Jewell and the buzz he felt from being "struck by lightning" was slowing to a "buh." He was thinking that maybe he had made a mistake and was about to go try to fetch the canoe and excused himself once more from Mrs. Smith.

He had barely gotten turned around when out bounded Miss Jewell onto the porch and down the steps. Her buzzing about returned the zest to his buzz, which confounded Mrs. Smith who really did want to have her other daughter married first.

"Mr. Dan!" Jewell shouted. "Where ya goin'?"

"Well, I'm headed down the creek to get the canoe. I'm hoping it doesn't have a hole in it."

"Do you mind if I come with you?"

Mrs. Smith quickly interrupted with "It don't matter if he minds. I mind and you ain't going!"

"Aw, Mama! We ain't goin' far . . . I guess Anna could come."

This set Mrs. Smith's wheels in motion. She thought it might not hurt at all if Anna went. Anna was quieter than Jewell and fairly well mannered. Perhaps the young man would overlook the fact that her lips could never cover her teeth.

"Yes, honey . . . I believe that would be okay. Tell Anna to come on out of the house and go with ya," Mrs. Smith said while finding her sugary side.

Jewell, who was not the least worried about competition from her sister, ran in and got Anna while Dan stood on the creek bank wondering if Anna could eat corn on the cob without opening her mouth. He didn't like hurting anyone's feelings, but he didn't want to hurt his own either especially thinking that a kiss from Anna might turn into a bloodied mess.

The two girls came from behind the house with Jewell leading a big Billy goat as Anna was carrying a long line. Dan was beginning to wonder if all three of the inhabitants were crazy.

"Miss, I don't mean to sound doubtful, but why are you leading that Billy goat?" asked Dan with a hint of confusion.

"Mister, I kinda knew you were going to ask me that. When we get down stream close enough to your canoe, I'm going to swim across and tie that line that Anna is holding to the canoe and then I'm going to swim back and tie the other end to the goat. That means that the goat is going to be responsible for pulling your canoe back across an' upstream until you get into the still waters where it won't wear you out to paddle on back upstream to wherever it is you're going. Now you could've just watched and then you woulda learned something and I wouldn't have had to give you such a long soliloquy. Do you have any more questions?" asked Jewell authoritatively.

"How'd you know it was on the other side?"

"You came back without it, didn't ya? An' I know this creek, an' I'll betcha it's in the rushes, isn't it?"

"Yep, that's where it is," Dan replied, being impressed by Jewell's "smarts."

"Any more questions?"

"Well . . . Why did you go get into dry clothes if all you gonna do is get wet again?"

Jewell didn't particularly like that question and said, "I was just doing what my mama told me, which is what a body should always do! Now, have you got any more questions?"

"No, ma'am," Dan replied meekly while shaking his head.

"Where did you put in?" asked Jewell.

"I'd say . . . Maybe a mile or two back."

"That's what I figured. Sounds like you put in at Rich's landing. Did you bring your canoe out on a truck?"

"Yes, ma'am."

"You can walk back and get the truck if you want to, but it's rough going along the creek bank. You see that road right over there? You could even walk that and get your truck. It's about three miles going that way though."

"Herbert and me didn't have no trouble paddling upstream yesterday. I suspect I can just paddle it on up. I thank you for your advice though," replied Dan as he was regaining his dignity.

"Well, your clothes weren't dripping wet yesterday either, were they?"

"Not at all," Dan replied with a wry grin.

Dan and Jewell changed the conversation to small talk, which Anna observed with painful resignation. She ran on ahead of them, bellowing that she would never get married.

"I'm sorry to hear that your father died last year," Dan said with genuine feeling.

"Yes, thank you . . . He had a heart attack. He lived a few more days . . . He tried to get out of bed one evening and just killed over.

I had just turned fourteen. I won't ever forget that birthday," Jewell said solemnly.

"My father died right before I turned fifteen from a heart attack. Seems like everybody in his family died of a heart attack."

"So we were both fourteen when our daddies died and from the same thing."

"Well, I was . . . Yes, I was still fourteen," Dan replied as he realized that Jewell was weaving the tapestry of a common bond and he was not about to unravel it before it even got started.

They talked on a while longer after the goat had successfully pulled the canoe upstream to the calmer water. Dan pulled the canoe onto the bank and continued the conversation.

"Jewell, I wired my mother a day or two ago that I was coming home . . . I don't have a job here, but if I had a reason, I sure would get one. That's one thing I know how to do is get a job. I don't care about farmin'. Looking at the back end of a mule team while driving a wagon is bad enough, but I ain't gonna walk behind one and hafta keep sidesteppin' the 'fertilizer,' if you know what I mean? That's for sure! Now, tell me, do I have a reason to stay here?"

"Not just yet, young fella!" cried out Mrs. Smith from behind a large oak tree.

"Mama! Please, can't we do this proper? He knows that I had to give him reason to ask your permission, so don't run him off!" Jewell pleaded.

"You let him get a job first! Then we'll talk! I don't want no drunken buzzard hanging around here livin' off our scraps . . . He's gonna have to earn his keep!"

"Mama! Who says he's gonna be living off our scraps? It's time for me to move on, Mama! I suspect this young fella is gonna want his own place, and if I marry him, you can't expect me to not go with him or anyone else that I marry!" protested Jewell.

"What do you mean anyone else?" asked Dan.

"Oh, that's just to shake her up a little bit," replied Jewell as she slapped Dan on his forearm.

"Well, it shook me up a little bit."

"Don't let it," she replied as she looked softly into his eyes. "Look, Mama, I'm fifteen years old, and by the time we get married, if we do, I'll be sixteen. I don't want to be an old maid!"

Anna, who was standing behind a bush and could hear everything, began to cry and ran back to the house, loudly stating, "Jewell! What does that make me? I hate you!"

Dan was saddened a little bit that poor Anna was not married, but they were all witness to the fact that natural selection can be cruel sometimes, and it was not Dan's fault that only 50 percent of Mrs. Smith's daughters were of the marrying kind. He was satisfied that his excursion was a success and he decided that it was time to go and that he would paddle the canoe upstream to the truck. Yesterday he had Herbert to help him paddle, but he figured that he could manage because he wouldn't have to paddle Herbert's weight.

They all said their good-byes and Mrs. Smith asked Dan when he would be back. He wasn't sure because he didn't know when he could borrow a truck, car, or wagon to get back out there, but he assured them that he would be back, hopefully with a new job.

To begin with his trip upstream was easy paddling, but as his endorphins began to wane so did his energy. He was determined, however, to dig in and continue his slog back to the truck.

When he got to the truck and loaded the canoe, which had suddenly gotten very heavy compared to its virtual lightness from that morning, he realized that he had been there longer than he meant to. Herbert would be getting off work in about an hour and Dan had promised that he would return the truck soon after lunch time.

When he pulled into the stone yard of Diomatti Monument companies (yes, that's right, two companies with the same name in the same location), Herbert was sitting on top of a stone waiting for him.

"It's about time you got here! Where have you been?" Herbert asked with a twinkle in his eye.

"You know good and damn well where I've been! I had a little accident on top of everything else. I ran your canoe right into a log, but don't worry, I didn't hurt it."

Herbert went over and skeptically inspected the canoe and was satisfied that Dan told the truth. He looked back at Dan for several moments and mischievously thought that he might not tell him that he asked one of the Diomatti brothers if they would give him a job.

"Say, Herbert, I kinda hate to ask, especially since I took advantage of you today, but do you reckon I can get that job, going to pick up marble?" Dan asked.

After a couple of seconds of hesitation, Herbert relented and said, "As a matter of fact, I told Joe about you today and how reliable you were, even though I'm not so sure about that now. So he said for you to come on in the morning and he would talk to you about it. Now, going to pick up that marble ain't an everyday job, so you might want to tell him about what else you can do. If he likes you, then he'll find you some work, 'cause there is plenty to do."

"You can betcha I'll be here."

So Dan got started in the monument business in a small way. It turned out that it wasn't full-time, but it didn't matter because there was a company from Italy that was building a new textile mill in Hamburg and they were going to need plenty of laborers.

***

Into the Life Real

It took him a month to settle in to both occupations. It was a struggle at times, but he was able to do it and he bought a small three-fourths worn-out car and drove it on down the road adjacent to Johnson's Creek to the Smith homeplace to tell Jewell that he was not going back to Birmingham and that he was going to be able to court her "proper."

The dirt road to Jewell's house was long and winding. It was obvious that the zigzagging old road was not engineered, but instead evolved in a very haphazard way. Instead of knocking down a tree or digging up a huge boulder or even moving a dead cow, the road builders just went around them, creating something of a mystery to future travelers.

Dan was chugging along at around twelve miles an hour when he came to another road that turned off to the right. It was basically the driveway to Jewell's house, but he had not seen it from that side and did not realize it so he chugged on past.

He drove about a half mile and was beginning to wonder just how far down this blooming road she lived. Much to his chagrin, at a half mile and twenty-six feet, the road ran out at the creek and it was mushy as hell! Most of the cars that a young man of twenty could afford really didn't have brakes, but don't worry the mush stopped it before it went into the water.

He tried to back out but it wouldn't go. He got out and decided to leave it running since he would be standing in a terrible quagmire halfway up to his knees if he had to go around to the front to restart it. A little mud was not about to shake his confidence so he started his trek back to Jewell's house on foot with the firm belief that he was going to make her his wife.

When he got close enough to her house, he could hear the cheerful noise of a couple of teenage girls and a young man. He wondered if some fool had been hoodwinked into courting Anna. When he got even closer, he didn't particularly like what he saw.

Jewell was having a grand old time and was giving a young man in his army uniform a grand old hug. The one thing that growing up tough didn't do for Dan was to teach him humility. The muscles in his face tightened and his hackles were raised; he was poised for a fight.

"Jewell!" Dan shouted when he got close enough.

Stunned, Jewell turned to face him. "Dan! Where in the world did you come from?"

"I came from back yonder. I bought a car—"

"You bought a car! That was you that drove by in that stinky old thing a minute or two ago?"

"Yep! I bought an automobile and drove it down here and I missed your house and I drove it right into the mud."

"Well, Dan, why did you drive it down here, do tell?"

"I think you know why. I've come to court you, but I reckon it's too late!"

Jewell, Anna, and the soldier couldn't help but laugh. Mrs. Smith came out of the door wiping her hands on her apron and, upon seeing Dan's expression, threw her head back with even greater exuberance.

"What in thunder is so funny?" asked Dan with incensed puzzlement.

"You are!" cried Jewell.

"Do you mind telling me what it is that's so funny about me?"

"I do declare, Dan! You drove your automobile into the mud! I've seen you all of three times and all three times it seems that you have made something of a fool of yourself!"

A deep frown accentuated Dan's brow, and he was about to really lose his cool, which he did from time to time, but it usually took a lot to do it. He ripped the hat off his head and stuttered a few unintelligible words, as he pointed it at the young man.

"Now, Dan, I do believe that you are concludin' something that might be a wee bit in the wrong direction!" Jewell interrupted him sarcastically. "This here is my brother Ira. He's just getting out of the army and he's come home, so what do you have to say for yourself?"

"I . . . uh . . . uh . . . well . . . Dad-gum-it, Jewell! How is a fella to know?"

"I believe the saying might be 'keep your mouth shut and you might learn something.' Seems like we had this conversation before."

"Yes, Jewell," Dan said while casting his eyes down in humiliation. Maybe growing up hard didn't teach him humility, but apparently Jewell would.

"It's okay, Dan. Surely your whole life is not one big mess up after another. I think I'd like to see you enough to know that for sure," Jewell said with compassion.

Dan looked up at her hesitantly at first and then he began to smile. Jewell liked his smile; it *was* an infectious smile and she returned it in kind. Their smiles turned to laughs, which of course caused the cynical Mrs. Smith to buck and come up with some snide comment. It's not worth mentioning what it was because the young lovers ignored her anyway.

"Dan, won't you come up on the porch and sit a spell?" Jewell asked.

"I would, except I left my little automobile running and I need to get it out of the mud."

"I'll go harness up the horses," Ira volunteered.

Jewell, Dan, Anna, and Mrs. Smith all started the walk ahead of Ira to go to Dan's car. Dan and Jewell walked ahead of the other two, talking to get to know each other. Jewell asked a hundred questions, which Dan answered in honest fashion.

Jewell was impressed with his candor and decided that he just might be all right. She really didn't know if he was actually going to ask her to marry him, but she knew quickly that she would say yes. Even though there weren't a lot of men in her neck of the woods to choose from, she could still tell that he was an honest and sincere man.

The four pedestrians and Ira, who was riding on one of the horses, got to the smoke factory of an automobile at about the same time. Ira hopped off and turned the team around and backed them up to the car. He unwrapped a chain from the yoke and slogged under the car and hooked it around the rear axle.

"Boy! I wouldn't have one of these darn things! I don't see how in the world you can even breathe driving this thing," Ira exclaimed.

"Well, I'm still living in a hotel where I can park this thing right out front, but you can't park your blame horse or your blame mule on the street! I don't know if you know it or not, but horses are on their way out," Dan retorted.

Jewell was pleased by Dan's vision of the future. She did not want to be stuck in a cabin on a farm for the rest of her life. She felt like that he was a risk taker, that with the right support might make something of himself.

"Aw, you're crazy! You ever seen a horse stuck in the mud? A horse has got more sense than a man driving an automobile. A horse'll stop before he gets in too deep."

"Well yeah! I have seen a horse get stuck in the mud and we took the truck and pulled him out. It broke its blame leg and we had to shoot it anyway!"

"Ah, horseshit!" exclaimed Ira.

Dan was beginning to see red and was biting his lip, but if Ira said one more thing, he was going to punch him out. Jewell saw what was going on with him and calmed him by putting her hand on his forearm. Dan looked at her and saw her smiling eyes and became a better person on the spot.

Once they got the car out and turned around, Dan asked Jewell if she might go with him for a ride. Mrs. Smith said that was a wonderful idea; she had only been in an automobile a couple of times in her life. So she immediately got in . . . The front seat in fact.

Jewell and Anna got into the back and Ira said no thanks. They rode all the way back to the main road to Hamburg and Dan asked them if they would like to go on into town to which they all excitedly agreed, but the problem was by letting the little car sit and idle for better than an hour, it began to run out of gas.

As it coughed and sputtered and spit and spewed, Jewell leaned over the front seat and asked Dan if he might have forgotten something. You might imagine that Dan was turning red once again.

Dan was one of those people who didn't give up easily, but he thought that one of two things was happening. God was really testing him to make sure that he was willing to go through a lot of trouble to be married to this woman, or God was telling Jewell to run for the hills before it was too late!

"Well, young man," said Mrs. Smith, "looks like you're gettin' off to a kinda bumpy start."

"Yes, ma'am. I reckon I know when I'm licked," he said dejectedly while hoping that Jewell might yet give him hope.

"Who says you're licked?" Jewell asked matter-of-factly.

Dan just shrugged his shoulders and tapped the steering wheel with his fingers.

"Do you have a gas can, son?" asked Mrs. Smith.

"Yes, ma'am, I do, but how far do you reckon it is to a gasoline store?"

"Why, it ain't far at all. I walk into town every day nearly," replied Mrs. Smith.

Dan was amazed at this revelation because it was a good seven and one half miles into town which meant that Mrs. Smith walked nearly fifteen miles every day and that didn't even count all the walking around on her tiny little farm. He thought she was lying or at least exaggerating a bit, but Jewell indeed confirmed her claim. Dan figured that if he was going to marry this girl that he would have to believe her regardless of the facts. Still, Mrs. Smith actually did walk that distance nearly every day.

The gas can, which rode on the front fender behind the spare tire, actually had gasoline in it, much to Dan's surprise. He did not remember ever putting gas in it. He started to curse himself, but stopped, because he didn't want his passengers to think that he was a lunatic. Yet, what would they think if they knew his can had gas in it. It seemed to him that the best thing was just to put the gas in the car and go on.

The rest of the day went just fine. The rest of the week and the rest of the month and the rest of the year went just fine. They learned each other very well and even Mrs. Smith grew to love Dan.

Anna also found a suitor. Let's just say that they were a match made in heaven. God bless their children—they would not be pretty!

Dan, who was twenty-one, and Jewell, who was sixteen, were married with six of his nine siblings in attendance. Unfortunately his mother died a couple of months before the wedding. Jewell's brother and sister were there along with their mother. All in all there were around forty people in attendance.

As with any courtship, many memories were seared into their brains and the passage of time was gentle and the days seemed many. With marriage the whirlwind is not the romance but the brutal passage of time.

After ten months and every twenty-two months thereafter, the memories that they were creating all had to do with bringing brand-new Sanders into the world until there were seven. The last one coming in 1932, the year Roosevelt was first elected.

It was the Great Depression, but many parts of the South had never fully recovered from the Civil War and many Southerners couldn't tell a lot of difference because a lot of them were already living off watercress and chickweed. The soil in northwest Georgia was poor and rocky in many places and the yield from their crops was minimal. Most game was depleted and fishing the lakes and rivers was a very time-consuming endeavor without a huge return.

Dan, on the other hand, did know the difference and he knew how hard it was going to be to feed seven children. He set about doing whatever, whenever, and however he could to keep food on the table. Comparatively speaking, he was quite successful. His children ate very well and so did Mrs. Smith who was living with them by this time.

In 1938, he was given an opportunity to buy into a business that would provide not only him a living, but his eldest son and his sons for many years. As people are still fond of saying about this particular business, "people are always going to die."

It is a business that its product defiantly says to the ages, 'We were here. We mattered."

***

PART II

The Shop

As told by Dan's grandson

There is a road, in fact an avenue, named Clyburn. This avenue begins its journey at North Broad Street, and at its beginning, it passes by a once-popular barbeque restaurant that is now a community kitchen and over a railroad bridge named after one of the former, or should I say "late" owners (definitely not, former late owner, because as yet, as far as I know, he is still "late").

Shortly thereafter, it reaches a fork where to the extreme left of the fork sits a grocery store with a goofy pig on its sign that grins somewhat like a Newt Gingrich. Now, here me out, a Newt Gingrich's grin looks perfectly fine on him and I wouldn't disparage him one bit, but on a cartoon pig, it looks . . . definitely goofy.

Now that you have spent a little too much time looking at the pig you must continue on, or your journey will be too short and not very informative.

When you have taken the right fork, you will pass many houses and the municipal swimming pool on your left where once stood an elementary school (here we say "ellamintry skuwal") where first my father and then my brother went to school, who each had the same first grade teacher whom my father said was pretty old when he arrived there, and in between being a school and being a pool, it was a fire hall, but never a school for pool nor a pool hall.

Once past the pool you come to the intersection of Clyburn Avenue and Church Street, where no churches stood until an old package store was converted for the purpose of religion in 1983 (but

I don't believe the former owners were). On the same side of the road, as the pool, lies a cemetery (a large one, at that), and at the other end of the cemetery on the opposite side, in a near blind curve, sits our shop—a monument shop (a not-so-large one, at that) that our grandfather built in 1953. Next to our not-so-large shop on the right sits an even less-not-so-large (that is to say, small) office, unless of course you are facing the cemetery and then the buildings are oriented very much the opposite way.

While you are facing the cemetery, you will notice a road, on the right, that traverses its way up a hill with little roads branching off to the left that will take you into the cemetery. After you have perused a few of the thousands of headstones, you may turn around, and while heading back to the shop, you will notice a church on your left in the corner of Clyburn, and after all of these years, I just realized that that road leading past the cemetery and to the school that replaced the old one, and into a subdivision, has no name! In fact this road that does actually lead somewhere is not even on a map and is claimed by no one.

All right, now that you are back at the shop, you will notice that the church is on your right and the cemetery is on your left, turn around, and you'll notice—okay, I'm being redundant (if you're byslexic I'm deing rebunbant.)

Looking at the shop, it resembles a pole barn with the poles having been made from the pipes of an old steam locomotive. You will notice in front of the shop building a row of stones. Looking between the shop and the office, you will notice even more stones that continue to the front of the office in two rows to a gap where the door is, and on around to the side you will notice even more stones.

After you have made your purchase, you may leave, feeling good about your decision, but if you just leave . . . well . . . we feel pretty dejected because it is surely difficult selling something that no one really wants and quite often one stone fits two or even three people just fine, but really, either way is just fine because, if something doesn't fit, then don't buy it.

After you leave our shop and continue away from our town, twelve miles later, you'll wind up in someone else's town, which is

Clyburn, and if you go on through, which only takes a minute (be careful because if it only takes you fifty-nine seconds you'll get pulled over and ticketed by a very intense policeman who is offended by the fact that you don't think enough of his town to slow down to actually see it), you will make your way to Capersville. If you make your way through Capersville traveling the Clyburn Highway, then you're damn good and can probably solve a Rubik's cube in sixteen seconds.

In the old days, and I mean "really old days," when the dust flew from the road in summer and the red clay melted down and much of it ran into the Wachamacallit (an old Indian word meaning: "too damn hard to pronounce") river with the winter rains, it was the main road to Atlanta. It was the same road that General William Tecumseh Sherman took his union troops through here on his way to amend the skyline of our afore-mentioned capital city. Might I add that he did a capitally fine job of originating the first real effort of urban renewal (probably the first in all the world) for our fine capital? He even left these great big bows made from train tracks for decorations all over Atlanta, and you know, from what I hear, nary a soul came out to thank those boys that did that!

Bring your mind back to the shop and you'll see a six foot high fence attached to the poles half way around and the rear half is corrugated tin that goes the whole twelve feet with a couple of dust-covered windows on the right end and windows at the rear that are completely covered in dust.

Go through the gate on the right side and you will see an enclosed layout room that is covered except for an opening in the middle, large enough to pull the bridge crane in and out, that allows us to place or remove the stones that we ready for sandblasting.

Parallel to the frontward most side of the layout room is a partition that divides the front and rear of the shop with an opening between it and the layout room. At the other end of the partition is an opening between it and the compressor room. In the beginning, the old 1917 compressor was water cooled by the same water line that serviced the office. In the summer, when the compressor was pushed a bit too hard, it would cause the toilet tank lid to flap like an angry politician. Once, the lid blew all the way open and filled the office with steam!

At the rear inside wall just outside of the layout room is the sandblaster, which was the last thing installed. The date inscribed in the concrete base: August 12, 1953. So that is when we count the shop's birthday.

Dad was sandblasting a stone in the fifties during a thunderstorm when lightning ran into the building through the power lines to the electric motor that turned the compressor. It then jumped to the compressor and ran through the metal air line from the compressor to the sandblast generator and through the rubber hose and out through the nozzle into the sandblast booth where it ran several laps and died of exhaustion. With his hair standing straight up, he raced to turn off the compressor to the exclamation that what he witnessed was both pretty and frightening, which, I'm fairly sure, is where the expression "pretty frightening" comes from.

The only real change the shop has gone through in sixty-three years is the insult of aging.

We have patched it now and again as you would your old favorite pair of overalls. Did you ever pull the eyes off your Teddy bear and pull out the stuffing and roll it around in the dirt and stomp it and so forth? It's an old staggering drunk that is in dire need of intervention, but still, anyone who saw it in 1953 recognizes it today.

The shop that was here in 1942, before our present one, began life as a service station, which had a fairly steady business. In 1941 a new highway to Atlanta was finished, so the service station's business sort of steadied out. So the owner, out of desperation, approached my grandfather about purchasing his property so that he could buy another to relocate his station because the main flow of traffic had moved over to the new highway.

My grandfather could make a sow's ear out of a silk purse when he was negotiating a deal in his favor, so it was actually an obscenely low price. It was so low in fact that some detractors thought he must have extorted the property, but my grandfather really was not bent that way. Dan (my grandfather) started the negotiations by telling

Cecil that he was satisfied where he was, because he really didn't want to work too close to home and because all he had to do was walk across the street from his house to get there. Of course this statement didn't make any sense at all to Cecil, but you will understand in a bit why he made it. (The church you see now was the house.) However, he decided that he would take it off Cecil's hands even though he couldn't think of what he might do with it, but of course, he knew what he could do with it.

Nevertheless, he convinced the owner that it would only be useful to another monument dealer who would not want to compete with him. Since Dan was the sexton of the cemetery, he would have the advantage over any competitor, so you see, it would just be useless to try to sell it to anyone else because they would default on it in less than six months.

The deal was made, money was exchanged, and Dan moved his little company. The "drag" came in just barely a year because my grandmother *could* keep up with everything he did.

One particular instance of his dissatisfaction with being too close to home involved two attractive widows who never seemed to tire of coming by to "thank" Dan for the "outstanding" job that he had done on each of their husband's monument. Of course all Dan did was to sell, with the rest of the company doing the "fine" work, but he didn't want to discourage such a thoughtful gesture, so he invited them to "carrying on" the practice. (Turned out, Dan encouraged carrying on quite a bit.)

Normally one widow at a time would drop in, but on this fine spring day, with the sap rising in flora and fauna alike, both dropped in at the same time just as Dan was about to leave after closing and they seemed to begin a competition for Dan's attention. He stopped, of course, not wanting to be rude, so he stood and talked to them for some time.

My grandmother, innocently enough, yelled from across the street that supper was ready.

Dan smiled and nodded and kept on talking and the ladies talked back and they were having a grand ol' time with full-bodied laughter and vigorous arm patting and the showing of lots of teeth and Dan shifting one leg over the other as he leaned on a tomb-stone and then stood up for a second and then leaned back down again, and one lady leaned against the tombstone next to Dan so she could touch his arm better and Grandmother had had enough. Seven o'clock, out she came, frying pan in hand, with her eyebrows definitely drawn toward the middle and a determination to drop Dan's sap back down to his sox. A blind man could have read the look on her face and felt the heat coming from it too!

"I called you three times and you're making a fool out of your-self out here and your children can see you and you gals ought not to make such a fuss over a forty-three-year-old married man with seven children . . ." (some of my aunts and uncles said she said "damn fool," but I can't bring myself to believe it, not from St. Jewel.)

That was enough information to convince them to leave and for Dan to lose his appetite and to decide that a new house was indeed precipitously within his budget.

***

Now, the way he derived the monument company in the first place is a little cloudy, but the story I heard with the most consistency is that he had gone to Tate (that's Georgia) for several years and picked up marble and delivered it to two brothers, Joe and Frank Diomatti, who were actually competitors who shared opposite ends of the same building. They even shared the same employees, who were loyal to both, or neither, and who always kept their mouths shut, and the same bridge crane, which was rolled by hand from one end of the building to the other, so if one was loading his truck and turned his back for a mere 3.1 seconds, often, the other would come and get the crane to move something small enough to have picked it up by hand and carry it two miles without even getting out of breath. Of course in the 1930s that could have been fairly heavy—their bones were better and they didn't know they shouldn't.

Neither brother had any qualms about appropriating the other's tools or stones or customers so there was always a battle brewing. One excuse that they were always absconding with the other's stuff was because they had never decided a clear-cut division between the two sides of the building, and every time they did "decide" where the line was, one or the other would move his gear a little over the line, and the other would move it back and place some of his gear a little over on his brother's side.

This battle, which started around 1918, as a matter of course, went on for years, until late September of 1937 when their two wives, which they did not share, told them that if they could not come to an amiable agreement as to where the true center line was, that they knew it was in there somewhere, they would have to sell out, or they would be out on their derrieres.

Since "London Derriere" was one of their favorite tunes this confused them, so realizing that they did not know what "derriere," meant they looked it up in the dictionary (which they did share) that was stuck under a pile of rubble. This helped convince them to rectify the problem.

Because they had taken over their father's business, they couldn't bear the thought of giving up their interest to anyone else, let alone to each other. So they spent some time trying to figure out how to divide it. Earlier I mentioned that their wives suggested an amiable solution, but of course that was like asking two tom cats to pat each other on the back and live in harmony, which cats will do, but their claws are fully extended and when they are through "patting" each other on the back the ground looks like the floor of a barber shop.

One would think that simply measuring from end to end with a tape measure and dividing it down the middle would have cured the conflict, but the shop was so piled up with old worn-out equipment, old stones, truck parts, and beer bottles, which belonged to one and not the other, that it was impossible.

They tried clearing a path through the middle so they could mark it, but it wasn't straight so the tape measure had to be bent, which would be totally inaccurate, which also caused a ruckus. So, since they trusted their feet more than they trusted an instrument designed expressly for the purpose of exacting distances, they decided to step it off heel to toe. (How stepping off the distance by foot was deemed more equitable is anyone's guess.)

The problem with using feet was that Joe wore a size eleven, because he wanted people to think that he had bigger feet than Frank (he wanted people to think that everything he had was bigger than Frank's), and Frank wore a size seven, and each wanted to use his own foot to make the measurement.

Joe told Frank, to begin with, that he would let him step it off and then they would divide it in two. Without thinking, this sounded okay to Frank so he started from his end of the building and stepped off one hundred and nine steps, sidestepping when necessary, as Joe followed right along to assist him with the counting, noting every time that Frank left the tiniest of space between his heel and toe so that at least three times Frank had to start over.

Joe, being the clever one, convinced Frank that since he had stepped off the entire distance, and since he wanted to be fair, that starting from his own end he would step off fifty-four steps and give him the half foot that was left over. Feeling that he had won a major concession, over these six inches, Frank agreed.

Joe stepped it off very rigidly, articulating each step so that the whole town could hear, while Frank was pointing at each step like a referee counting out a fallen boxer.

At the end of this endeavor, they drew a line in the dust (literally, for that was what the floor was made of due to the many years of stone carving) and shook hands. Both men smiled titanically—Frank, because he knew he had gotten an extra half foot, and Joe, because he knew Frank hadn't.

After the brothers shook hands, they headed for home. Each had an uneasy feeling. Joe never drank, but tonight he thought he needed one, not to celebrate, but to numb himself to the inevitable awakening of his brother's wrath. Frank thought he had won, but was worried that it had been too easy. The expected afterglow of the end of their prolonged conflict didn't materialize. It seemed more the end of an era.

It was the end of an era much the same way that a smoker quits smoking fifteen or twenty times a day. Wars never vaporize so quickly and this one wasn't going to either.

Frank got home and told his wife what had transpired, to which she was very proud. He kissed her on her forehead and went to bed without a drink, which he had not done since he was seven years old (or was it for seven years?). I told you, the story was cloudy.

Joe did a U-turn and headed back to the shop. The building sat on a slope and on the upper side was Joe's office where the entrance was on First Street. When you entered, you could overlook the interior of the shop down below through a row of windows and a wooden door with a large glass pane, which led inward onto a loft.

Frank's office was at the other end on the ground floor, which led out of the side and onto Second Avenue. It had been converted from a formerly large storage room with walls made of corrugated tin. One night, back around 1930, Joe had pulled the nails out of one of the panels of tin and cut the heads off just long enough to allow himself to sneak in and out of Frank's office, and then replace the tin and push the nails back in without having to hammer them. He would then lean an old, basically discarded, tall tombstone against the tin so that it wouldn't mischievously warp its way onto the ground leaving a gaping hole.

This actually happened once, just as Frank was leading a customer out to the display yard. He heard the "broing-bang" of the tin making its escape from the wall, but when he turned around to see what had happened all he saw was dust and the cat racing from the office! He also didn't notice Joe (who also had drilled a peephole in another piece of tin, standing on the other side trying to look innocent and trying to whistle an unmelodious tune, but his mouth was full of dust so it came out more of a "ptuey"). Mainly, Frank had not noticed Joe because his customer was a very beautiful young widow who needed his undivided attention.

Though this pseudo door was normally used for spying, the night of their compromise, it was used for pinching liquor. So after Joe's acquisition, he took his jug of moonshine back up the stairs to his loft to sit in an old parlor chair that he had put there so he could sit and relax a bit and survey his domain before going home.

As Joe expected, Frank awoke from a restless sleep with a jolt, realizing that two different shoe sizes gave two different results! "That son of a . . . ," he started to say, but owing to the fact that they shared the same mother, he realized that it would indicate a particular sense that he was one too!

Frank sprang from his bed, put on his shoes, and raced out of the house to confront his brother about this egregious misrepresentation of their agreement. He figured that Joe would either be at home or at Renaldo Garantini's garage playing poker until dawn, which was Joe's vice, especially when he was in a good mood, and he knew that Joe would be in a grand mood over his victory.

What Frank didn't know was that Joe was in a terrible mood and that he was beginning to feel a wave of remorse, which was due, in part, to the feeling that the moonshine was turning his skin inside out.

Joe decided that what he needed to help smooth the journey of the moonshine down his gullet was some "Vie-anny sawsijiz." So he went into his office and took down one of the twenty or so cans of Vienna sausages and returned to his chair.

This endeavor began to change his mood to the better. With a wry smile he opened the sausages, which alerted the cat, so he and the cat shared their little feast. The cat did, however, turn down the moonshine—sometimes cats are smarter than their people.

After a couple of cans and a little bit more than enough 'shine, Joe went to sleep as the cat was licking himself silly. After a brief interlude, the sausages alerted Joe that moonshine and animal intestines stuffed with spicy meat are not to be taken internally. It's all right to rub 'em on your face or your stomach, but you had better wear a surgeon's mask if you do.

Joe jumped up and stepped on the cat's tail as he was trying to bend over the railing to vomit! Screaming cats tend to make people jump, to which Joe was no exception, and well, the railing was kind of low, and apparently, Joe went right over it and landed on his . . . well, that's just it; he didn't land on anything. His big old shoe got hung in a crook in the railing.

His stomach forgot its marching orders for a half minute or so, but being dutiful, it came around to carrying out its mission. Because he was hanging upside down he began to "throw down" or "down chuck," if you prefer. Of course some of the Vienna sausages blitzkrieged their way into his sinus cavity.

So Joe was hanging there head down, getting sicker, and passing out with vomit stuck where it was never engineered to go. The cat was in no mood to stick around, so after turning and spraying Joe in retaliation for stepping on his tail, he went, with haughty indignation, to be comforted by a little pussy.

***

This was a very unexpected scene for my grandfather to come into and here's how he described it:

Back in 1937, in, I believe, late September, I had just gotten back home from moving a family up to Elliott Springs . . . that road was so rough . . . It took *all* day. My old truck wouldn't go fifty miles an hour on a good road, but up there, I couldn't go but fifteen, sometimes less than ten. That road would shake your eyeballs right out to the end of your nose. When I got back to the house, it was around eight thirty and I was about to eat pinto beans and corn-bread when Banga (my grandmother's nickname) told me that my ol' friend Herbert Watson at Hamburg Monument had called me to see if I could go get a load of granite in Elberton the next day. Well, you know back then it would take you two days to go there and back. If it hadn't been for the times it was, I would of not gone, but we still had a house full of youngans and if you could make a dollar you had to do it.

My old one-ton truck was over at Diomatti's where I kept it most of the time because I hauled more rock for them than everybody else put together . . . It still kind of ticks me off that I didn't get to eat supper that night . . . but if you want to get to Elberton before dark, you gotta get on the road by four o'clock in the morning.

Well anyway, I had to take the tag off my three-quarter–ton truck because I didn't have money for two tags . . . The police were always trying to catch me with the tag on the wrong truck, but they never did . . . so I took the tag on over to Diomatti's, and when I got there, I noticed that the lights were on in the shop. See, they had a closed in building but you could see lights through some of the nail holes in the tin.

They never worked 'til dark so I thought something might be wrong. I was on Joe's side of the building, which was on the high side. So I went in, you know, nobody ever locked their doors back then.

Well, when I got in there, I could see Frank fightin' with the crane . . . looked like he was in there trying to move everything out of the middle of the building . . . piling off to each side.

When I walked in onto the balcony I saw a leg attached to a boot, stuck in the railing and another leg hangin' kinda loose, sorta waving gently back an' forth. I investigated a little further and saw it was Joe.

I said, "Joe, what in hell are you doin'?" to which he didn't say a thing. He just mumbled real low, so I knew he was alive.

So I hollered at Frank, "Frank, what in hell is Joe doing?"

"I don't give a good damn what he's doing . . . but what he's done is cheated me," he said before he turned around.

When he did turn around, he saw Joe hanging upside down and I declare if he didn't say "gaw dam it, Joe! If you're gonna hang yourself, you should do it from the other end."

Joe started coughin' an' gaggin' an' spittin' a little too! That's when I said, "Frank, don't you think we ought to get him down?"

And Frank said, "Hell, let him hang there. I don't give a damn if he dies!"

To which I said, "I think he might, his color looks a little off."

"Good!" was all he said.

To which I said, "Frank! If you don't help me get him down from here this instant, I'm going to bust your head wide open with that pry bar over there!" and I'd a done it too.

So Frank said "aw hell!" and went and got a rope.

I walked down to underneath Joe and saw that his hands were danglin' just above my head and I couldn't reach him so I told Frank we'd better pull him up, instead of lettin' him down case if that rope slipped one of us would have had to be on the ground while the other stayed up top so it would be easier for both of us to pull him up.

So we got up top and Frank looped the rope around Joe's legs an' made a lasso and slid it down to his arm pits, then he cinched it real tight, enough so to make Joe spit up some more.

When Joe's foot got hung in that railing, it twisted him around to where he was facing away from it, so when we pulled him up it folded him up like a folding chair. Well, when we got him up good enough to pull him over the railing we saw that his foot was twisted even worse than to start with.

When Frank tried to get Joe's foot unstuck, it wouldn't budge so after about five minutes of fighting with it, he reared back and gave it a swift kick, which caused the railing to break loose and Joe to go right with it.

Luckily we had tied the rope off on a rafter so Joe didn't hit the floor, but when we had got him up to the railing, the rope had slid down to about his middle. So when he stopped, it jerked some more of his content out onto the ground—it sure did stink!

The way Frank tied the rope allowed us to lower him down, right in to his own puke— whew!

About then Joe started comin' aroun' so the first thing I said to him was "Joe, your piss smells just like a cat's."

"What the fuh . . . what the fuh?" was all he could say.

Frank came back an' threw a whole bucket of water on him to clean him up and revive him too. It worked a little more to wake him up than it did to clean him, but he got up all right on his own.

Frank's fire was beginnin' to simmer down so he asked, kinda gentley, if Joe was all right.

Joe said, "Yeah, I'm all right," then he let out the sourest smellin' damn burp you've ever smelt.

"Good gawd-a-mighty, Joe! What in hell have you been drinkin'?" asked Frank.

"I been drinkin' yer shine an' eatin' vie-anny sawsijiz," Joe told him with his eyes about half open . . . You ever seen people with rubber band eyelids? That's what I call 'em. They can't open their eyes so they stretch their lids real slow an', when they go about as far as they can, their eyes just kinda pop open. That's what Joe kept doin'.

Well, to make a long story short, Joe came down with a sinus infection that turned into pneumonia and he died about two weeks later. Frank was so torn up that he tore the place down and sold all his equipment. I bought as much of it as I could, but I didn't have anywhere to put it so I went to Watson and asked him if I could keep it there at his place. It was mostly hammers and chisels and a few air grinders and such, so he said sure.

After a few months Watson asked me if I'd be interested in getting in the monument business. Since the Diomatti's were gone, he had more business than he could take care of and he knew I had some business savvy.

At that time he was just looking for a partner, but after about six months, his mother got real sick and he wanted to move back to his home to be near her so he offered me the whole deal, which I reckon you know how that turned out. Yep, just me and the bank owned it then. It just fell in my lap, and there was plenty of times I wished it hadn't. You think you're in the rich house one month and you're in the poor house the next. I'm just happy I was able to pass it on to my boy.'

***

The Folly of Fate

I t just so happens that that "boy" my grandfather was talking about was my dad. Granddad had boys, but after they got a taste of the bitter fruits of the stone business, the other two realized that they hadn't the talent to be able to stick it out. They both wanted something "better." Boy, did they miss out on a lot of fun!

My father, on the other hand, was loyal to my grandfather to a fault. He took over half the business when my grandfather retired and stuck it out until he was eighty-seven years old. Death was the only thing that stopped his tenure. He had always wanted to do other things, but it seems that once all that granite and marble dust gets into your system, it is hard to get away from it, probably because it hardens your brain. (I've always said that it's the spirit world that picks out certain fools and locks them into this infernal vortex. How many people grow up wanting to be in the monument business?)

When my dad started working in the monument business, he had quit a very promising job as a quality control foreman in the textile industry. My grandfather had asked Dad to go to work for him, but my dad resisted. Unfortunately, seemingly so at the time, my grandmother stepped in and convinced Dad that his dad needed him badly.

The truth is that my grandmother needed my dad to look after her husband, thinking that a son could keep the father from straying. Of course Dad had no real control over Dan and he wasn't much of a tattletale either so he pretended that everything was okay.

Dad worked for about a year and was being paid less than everyone else there, so one day he just didn't show up. He had already gone out seeking other employment and was offered a job making $10 a week more than what my grandfather was paying him.

My grandfather was pissed off at his ungrateful son, but my grandmother interceded one more time and basically blessed out my grandfather. "Dan! He's your son for crying out loud! If you can't pay him what you pay everyone else, then I don't blame him for getting another job!"

"Jewell, he knows that I'm going to give him this business when I retire . . ."

"That don't matter, Dan! He's just gotten married and he's gonna need a living wage. Nobody can live on what you're paying him, or are you gonna retire next week?"

"No! Of course not! I'm gonna work until I'm sixty-two."

"I guess you must want him to starve then? And his wife too! What if he has children? Are you wantin' to starve your grandchildren?"

Boy! That got him. Grandpop paid Dad twelve dollars more a week and there it was. Dad got sucked into the vortex and brought his unborn sons with him.

***

When my father was a teenager and had gotten his first car, which did not have any working brakes, but like most teenagers, he was too impatient to wait until he could afford to get them fixed before he could drive it. One day his friend Julius drove up to the house to see his new car.

"Hey, Norm, that's a nice car. What say we go for a ride?"

"I can't, Julius, my brakes don't work."

"What if we just drive around the block real slow, and when we get back around here, you just pull in real easy to the yard and cut the engine."

"I guess we could do that. I guess I could put some cinderblocks in the yard, and when I pull in, I'll just run into them and maybe that'll help stop us."

"Oh yeah, that'll work. Or we could just jump out once you aim it into the yard and we'll run around to the back and grab a hold of the bumper and drag our feet. That will probably stop it."

So off they went around the block at about ten miles an hour. Dad didn't want to go any faster in case a kid or a cat or dog or even an old lady might run out in front of the car. The ride was uneventful, and they got back to the house without incident and pulled into the yard. Dad cut the engine right before he hit the cinderblocks and Julius got out and ran around and grabbed hold of the bumper just as the engine let out tremendous backfire, which caused him to turn loose. With the lack of speed and everything else involved, the car stopped . . . when it hit the house.

Grandmother, great-grandmother, and his brothers and sisters all came screaming out of the house. Dad simply apologized and blamed Julius.

"Was he driving the car?" demanded Grandmother.

"No, ma'am."

"It doesn't matter whose idea it was! You are responsible!"

"Yes, ma'am."

"Now get that thing off my house!"

"Yes, ma'am."

They pushed the car away from the house, but this little ride around the block, along with the fact that it was red and a "real looker," created a real itch for my father and his friend to get the car out onto the road. They sat for a few minutes studying the situation and then Julius came up with another brilliant idea.

"Norm, what you say I drive in front of you and then when I stop, you'll stop when you run into me?"

You might think that my father would have hesitated a moment to think about this idea due to the complete and utter failure of Julius's first idea. You might be wrong; my dad had no qualms about running into the back of Julius's car.

They practiced a little while by going around the block. Julius would give plenty of distance before he would have to stop, which allowed my father to slowly bump into his car. Julius would then apply the brakes, gradually slowing both cars which gave them plenty of distance to stop. Of course sometimes he would get a little bit too much distance, and getting a little nervous, he would abruptly hit the brakes, slowing too quickly! *Bam! Bam! Bam! Bam! Bam!* Julius's car stopped! Dad's car bounced off one last time and then rolled gently against Julius's car.

To begin with, every day that they did this crazy thing, their necks and backs and arms and all would be so very sore. But they kept doing it. What do you expect? They were idiot kids, probably not that much different than kids are now.

Eventually they got to the point where they would drive all over town using this insane method. Once when they were stopped at a traffic light, a policeman, who was on foot, walked up to the cars and asked the two young gentlemen what in the hell was their idea. They were both very cordial as they didn't want their parents to knock the bajeebers out of them when they got home and assured the officer that everything would be fine, that they had practiced quite a bit, and were in no potential harm.

The policeman looked at both of them warily, but then just told them to be careful. The policeman also told them both that he had done some crazy things himself in his youth and lived to tell about it, so what the hell.

As I said, this insane method was working quite well—except Julius took a wrong turn and had them heading down a steep hill! He had accidentally knocked his car out of gear causing it to freewheel. My father had laid back, which had created quite a distance between them.

Julius was having trouble getting his car to slow down, but then when he got to the stop sign, he stood up on his brakes and managed to stop it just before going into the street! My father was going a good twenty-five miles per hour at this point, and when he hit Julius's car, it did knock him out into the street, literally. Julius went flying over the front of the car and onto the street! It was a minor miracle that he wasn't run over. He did get up limping but swore that he was okay.

My grandfather heard of this insanity when he got home from work. He summoned my father, who wondered what sort of punishment he might receive, but my grandfather directed him with a wave of his hand to get into the family car. He drove them straight to the Ford dealership and bought my dad his brakes with the stipulation that he would work it off.

For my dad it was bittersweet. He would have to become a normal driver; he never would have so much fun driving a car again.

Toward the end of Julius's life, my dad and I used to see him often at our favorite restaurant. The poor devil could barely move and had to use a walker. I never asked my dad if he thought that maybe all those rear-end collisions might have had something to do with Julius's condition. But it was Julius's idea in the first place to pull double duty with the brakes!

So you see? It may be that insane behavior is one of the things that the spirits who are in charge of the monument business are looking for.

***

Gone, But Not for Fartin'

Ron Anderson fit the bill and was quite a character. He was one of the cutters that granddad had recruited in Tate. Whenever he was instructed to cut "Gone, but not Forgotten" on a stone, he would say, "Gone, but not for fartin'." He was usually not involved with customers, but once when one asked for the aforementioned verse in his presence, he almost repeated back the bastardized version, but fortunately my grandfather, who was standing next to him as he was about to say it, stepped on his foot with his sledgehammer of a shoe! The customer, not having noticed this preemptive strike, must have thought that Ron was a sensitive sort, having seen his aggrieved expression.

One Monday in the 1950s, Ron did not come in to work until after lunch. When asked why he was so late, his reply was that he had "got into a ditch" the night before and couldn't get out so he stayed all night until help arrived.

My father asked him how badly had it hurt his car to which Ron replied, "I wasn't in my car . . . I just walked into it and fell down and couldn't get out." Ron was an Olympic-caliber drinker, but sometimes it made him a little "tired."

Another time, when the temperature had been down in the single digits for about a week, Ron convinced my grandfather that it was just too cold to work and asked him if it was okay if he went home. My grandfather agreed because he had noticed that morning that his lake had frozen solid and he would just as soon send him home as to pay him for sitting in front of a fire.

After a couple of hours, my grandfather told my dad that he thought he would just go on home too. When he got halfway up his driveway, which overlooked the lake, he could see Ron sitting out on the ice on a bucket next to a hole that he'd probably frozen his ass off to cut.

My grandfather drove down to the lake and rolled his window down and angrily hollered at Ron, "Ron, what the hell are you doing out here? I thought you said it was too cold to work!"

"Mr. Sanders, I ain't workin'! I'm fishin'. I wanted to see what it was like. Was wonderin' if this is where they get fish sticks!"

My grandfather just shook his head and was slightly amused at Roy's audacity and asked him, "Well, how is it?"

"Hell! It ain't worth a damn!"

"All right, well, if you catch anything bring 'em on up to the house and we'll fry 'em up."

Needless to say, Ron never made it up to the house. Let's just say that the fish had a hell of a lot better sense than Ron.

That Son of a Bitch

My grandfather was one tough son of a bitch. Not only did he endure being stuck in the mine for thirty-six hours and working from dawn to dusk during the Depression to raise seven children, he also had two heart attacks before he was sixty years old, one of them was when my father was with him on the main street in Gadsden, Alabama.

When he went down, my dad tried to help him up, thinking that he had just fallen. My grandfather told my dad to leave him there a minute; he would be all right. In due time he got up and told my dad that they should just go back to Hamburg. He refused my dad's pleas to go to the hospital and in time got better on his own.

In the 1950s, right after I was born, he was pulling a tractor up onto a flatbed truck when it flipped over backwards, breaking his back. My grandparents were thirty miles out in the country away from any hospital. My grandmother had to drag him into her car to get him to the hospital. It took a while to get better, but he didn't give in and went back to work as soon as he was able.

Even though he was very tough, he had his vulnerable side too. Somehow or another it always seemed to involve the opposite sex. It was usually because they distracted him and one such tale, indeed did show that he was human.

My grandfather always walked with his hands in his pockets and his head down. He would only raise his eyes every few feet to see where he was going and would look back down at the ground and keep going.

The bank where he did his business had both a front and a back door that was accessible to the customers. Grandfather always liked going in and out of the back door. This always gave him the opportunity to speak to everyone as he walked over to his favorite teller whom he thought was a very pretty woman.

The very pretty lady on this particular day paid close attention to my grandfather. Some say that she was somewhat flirtatious, which always distracted my grandfather even more.

The back door was at the end of a moderately long hallway, and as my grandfather started down it after he finished his business, he glanced back at the teller, which she briefly returned. Of course his juices, as they quite often did, stirred considerably.

When he turned around to walk out he noticed a man coming toward him and said to himself, "What about that . . . That man looks just like me!"

He continued walking and noticed the man was coming directly at him and so he stepped to one side, but so did the other fellow. So my grandfather stepped the other way and so did the other man.

"That son of bitch is gonna walk right into me!"

BHAM! Two of the bank workers ran over to him to help him to his feet! He had not actually walked down the hallway, but instead he had walked into the bank vault and straight into the vault mirror! Of course they apologized to my grandfather for not stopping him, but they were so used to him being in the bank that they thought he was just curious and wanted to see what was in there.

He thought it was nice that they trusted him. He said that he would've been a lot less embarrassed if they hadn't. After he steadied himself, he decided to go out the front door and nodded to everyone who was standing in polite silence as he walked out.

Once out onto the street, he placed his hat on his head and turned confidently to go back to his car. Of course he heard the now unrestrained laughter coming from the bank.

"That son of a bitch!" he said with a growing smile and a single shake of his head.

***

Where's Bull?

There is no question as to where Bull got his name. Large nostrils, large head, furrowed brow, massive shoulders and arms, very thick legs. He was a very frightening-looking individual, however, he was as gentle as a lamb. This didn't keep people from being intimidated by him.

Once, when four fairly strong men were struggling to load a very heavy wood-burning stove as Bull was walking by, he stopped and asked if he could help. They all scoffed at him and turned back to try again. They tried to coordinate their movements but someone was always early or someone was always late. Ergo, it appeared that their plan was not to load a stove, but to practice a form of mutual torture.

When on the fourth try one of the men pulled a muscle in his back, Bull walked confidently over and simply "looked" the men out of his way. One also might say that the four men had a look of fright about them.

Bull reached to put his arms around the stove, which caused a very contemptuous reaction by the men who had failed miserably.

"What the hell! Does he think he's gonna pick up that stove by his self?" scoffed one.

Bent down, with his arms still around the stove, Bull glanced around at—as I said—the four miserable failures. With only a trace of a smile he began to lift the stove. Now, you might think he miraculously lifted it without even a meager grunt. No . . . a little more than that.

"Bull shit! He's gonna bust a gut!" mocked another.

Bull's veins were bulging, no doubt. His muscles were taught and with no further ado he lifted the stove onto the back of the truck.

He turned victoriously to face his new disciples without showing that he was out of breath, even though he was.

"No bull shit . . . jus' Bull. That's what they's call me," he said as he returned to his original plan.

One might have expected to see the four men applaud or attempt to pat him on the back or attempt other variances of praise and salutations, but they were in genuine awe and of course were afflicted with a sudden paralysis, which afflicts many when their pride has been hurt.

It so happens that my grandfather had been watching this afternoon's folly from across the street and having a good laugh. Of course when he saw Bull lift the stove onto the truck, he salivated at the idea of having him in his employ. He angled across the street with his unnatural one-leg-shorter-than-the-other gait and headed Bull off.

"Mister, that was one helluva display back there. Do you need a job? I'd really like to hire you."

"I has a job, sir, but I could always use a little extra money. I could he'p part time if that was tolerable," Bull answered without the first idea of what it was that he would be helping to do.

"I'd like you full time if I could, but if that's not in the cards, then I reckon I could maybe use you on some really tough jobs. When can you work?"

"Well, I can works on Wednesdays an' Fridays. They don't work us on Friday 'cause they used to pay us afore lunch an' lots o' the men wouldn't come back so as we now works Sattiday an' they pays us on Sundy morn in front o' our wives at the church so as nobody can go to the speak easy."

"So you are married?"

"Yessir, I is."

"She must be one stout woman!" my grandfather said as he was thinking that a small or frail woman might not survive even a single night of passion with Mr. Bull.

Bull hadn't a clue what my grandfather meant. They shook hands and my grandfather was surprised at the gentle control of Bull's handshake. Grandfather told him what his employment would be, which seemed to excite Bull, and they parted company.

The first day on the job Bull was ready, willing, and able to impress. He was sitting on one of the display stones when my father arrived at seven thirty. Dad asked if he could help him to which Bull, quickly getting to his feet, replied, "Naw, sir, I's here to help yous I reckon."

Needless to say, my father was impressed with his new employee. For one thing, while Bull was still sitting, he was as tall as my father, who of course was standing. For another, his arms were "diametoriously" much larger than my father's legs.

"Okay, well when everyone gets here this morning somebody is going to take you out to the cemetery and show you the ropes. Now when they tell you to do something, we expect you to do it."

"Yessir, that's 'xactly whats I plan to do. Yous won't get no problem from me!" replied Bull.

"I'm sure from the looks of you that you're gonna work out fine," said my father with his trademark twinkle as they shook hands.

"Yessir, I sures hope so."

Dad would have patted him on the back but he would have had to jump, or otherwise it might have appeared to Bull that he was getting a bit too familiar with his lower anatomy.

Mr. McFrey (pronounced "fry"), my dad and grandfather's partner, was always the one to take the new employee out to the cemetery, which always concerned both of them because Mr. McFrey was a total screw-up.

The first place that Mr. McFrey took Bull was to Rose Hill, which was on the other side of town. The marker that was to be placed was for a single individual and not very large. He instructed Bull where to dig and told him to keep going until he got back, for he was only going to get a cup of coffee on Broad Street, three hundred feet away.

First coffee, then a pastry a block down, then a newspaper across the street, then a chat with an old friend, then a stop at the tobacco shop, then a stop at city hall to talk to the mayor about his sewer problem at home, then a trip to the bank to make a deposit that he was supposed to have made two weeks ago, then a trip to the shop so that he could sit down and enjoy his morning cold coffee, pastry, and newspaper.

My father, who had been at his usual station in the layout room when Mr. McFrey arrived, went to the office and standing in the doorway asked casually, "Where's Bull?"

Mr. McFrey jumped up, spilling his coffee, tearing his newspaper, and squashing his pastry that had taken route to the floor. He hardly waited for my father to retreat from the door before he was out of the office and into his car. My father had to sprint rapidly to get into the car just as Mr. McFrey had thrown it into gear.

"Shit! Shit! Shit!" was all that Mr. McFrey could say.

"WHAT!" cried my father.

"Damn! Shit! Fuck! Motherfucker!"

"WHAT?"

"AH, HELL!"

When they finally entered the cemetery and turned the corner where Bull had been left, Mr. McFrey reiterated with an ocean-like spray coming from his mouth, "Damn! Shit! Fuck! MOTHERFUCKER!"

When the car stopped my father fell out rolling onto the ground convulsing with uncontrollable laughter. All one could see was an obviously mighty hole and the top of Bull's head and his shovel propelling dirt at a very high velocity onto an ever-increasing monumental mound.

"I reckon you told Mr. Bull here to keep on a goin' 'til you got back, huh?" asked my father, barely able to breathe, as he grabbed a shovel to help Bull refill the hole.

At about that time my grandfather, who was told of the hasty departure from the shop by Mr. McFrey and my father, pulled up in his old Packard and got out and slowly walked with hands in his pockets over to the spot and looked it over carefully, looking very concerned. He looked up, very slowly, at Mr. Mcfrey with a droll grin and didn't say a word.

"Dammit to fucking hell!" replied Mr. McFrey.

***

Of course you'd have to imagine that Mr. McFrey screwed up more than just this one time. And you're imagining would not be imagination at all, but in fact you would be quite factual.

How about the time that he took Colorado to the cemetery to show him where to dig. "Dig it right here," he said. So Colorado dug while Mr. McFrey sat in the truck and read his newspaper.

"Okay, Mr. Jim. I's done. I'll get the concrete while you check it."

Mr. McFrey, who was a little ticked off for not being able to finish the article he was reading, got out of the truck with his tape measure and checked the beautifully formed hole.

"It's not in the right place. Why didn't you dig it where I showed you?"

"I did, Mr. Jim! I dug right where you told me!"

"No, Colorado! You didn't! I told you to dig it right here," Mr. McFrey said while pointing to the ground.

Colorado filled the freshly dug hole back in and, after tamping it down, said, "Well hell! I'll dig it right here, but that ain't where you told me!"

"Yeah, you'd better, and yes, it is!"

So Mr. McFrey went back to the truck to finish his article and Colorado dug some more. Colorado announced that he was done and Mr. McFrey put down his paper and checked it again.

"Well, Colorado! Why didn't you dig it where I told you?"

Colorado was turning red and that's not easy for a black man. So he refilled the new hole and dug some more while Mr. McFrey finished his paper. After about fifteen to twenty minutes Mr. McFrey noticed that Colorado did not tell him that he was finished. When he looked up he saw Colorado leaning on the shovel with a bit of a snarl after he had dug a trench all the way across two graves.

"Now put the damn thing where you want it!"

Mr. McFrey fired Colorado right on the spot, but when the two returned to the shop my father and grandfather overrode him.

"Colorado, go on home . . . ," My grandfather said as he paused and looked at Jim.

Jim looked condescendingly with narrowed eyes at Colorado and said, "That's right, you get outta here and don't come back!"

Colorado hung his head, slightly cutting his eyes toward my grandfather and headed toward the door. Everyone in his community was proud of him for working at a place that they believed was closely connected to the spirit world. It was going to be tough for him to tell them that he stood up to a white man, but the white man that he trusted didn't stand up for him.

"Now, Jim, don't you reckon he at least needs to come back to get his money . . . That we owe him?"

"Well yeah, he can come back for that!" Jim said angrily.

"Well, if he comes back for his money, don't you reckon he ought to go set those four monuments that are sitting down there ready?"

"Well hell! Me and Norm can do it!"

"Oh no! I've got to go to Kennesaw tomorrow and meet with a family to make a good sale. I have no idea how long that's going to take," replied my father.

"Well, me and John can do it!" Jim argued.

Colorado saw what was going on and his hopes rose.

"Jim, two of those monuments down there are going to take four people and Colorado here is the best one of all of you!"

Colorado really wasn't one of the best, but my grandfather liked to dig at Jim McFrey whenever he could.

"Colorado, you come on back tomorrow. In the meantime I suggest you apologize to Mr. McFrey and shake hands," said my grandfather.

"Yes, sir . . . Mr. McFrey, sir, I do apologize. From now on I'll do exactly what you tell me and I won't argue neither."

Mr. McFrey relaxed a little bit and reluctantly took Colorado's hand and said, "All right then, you know all I try to do is make sure that we stick to the Hamburg Monument Company standards."

"Yes, sir, I understands," Colorado said as he turned and left to go home.

After Colorado got out of earshot my father told Jim, "Now, Jim, you know good and damn well it was your fault!"

"Now wait a minute! You don't even know what happened!"

"I don't have to, Jim! Remember Bull? His head barely sticking out of the ground!"

"Aw hell!"

***

One would also think that Mr. McFrey was not very fond of his fingers. This incident also involved Colorado: many times when a base was set onto the concrete, which was a dry mix, it would be slightly out of level. One of the methods that were used to get the stone into level was to take half of an old railroad tie and slam it down onto the high side.

Mr. McFrey was watching the level while Colorado was hammering down with the tie.

"Hit it right here!" said Mr. McFrey, as he was patting the stone where he wanted Colorado to hit.

Colorado reared back with the huge block of wood, and just as he was about to come down with it, Mr. McFrey would pat the stone again and say, "Hit it right here!" Colorado would have to put the piece of wood back to the ground because it was just plain too heavy to stand there and hold up around his head.

So Colorado would regroup and lift the heavy block up to his head again, and just as he was about to bring it down, Mr. McFrey would say as he was patting the stone, "Hit it right here!"

Now do you really believe Colorado did this on purpose? Surely not! Of course, he remembered that he promised Mr. McFrey that he would always do what he was told. On the fourth attempt that damn block got really heavy and came crashing down on Mr. McFrey's fingers!

Mr. McFrey didn't make a sound. He just stood up, and without looking at his fingers, he stuck them in his pocket. After that, for a solid week, he walked around with his hand in his pocket and would not take it out for love or money.

***

Back in the old days they used a skid-board to slide the monuments off the truck. A mere two months after Colorado crushed Mr.

McFrey's fingers, they were sliding a stone down to the ground. Mr. McFrey, being the screw-up that he was, was holding onto the bottom side of the stone instead of the top side, and when the stone reached the ground, Mr. McFrey's fingers were still under it. Ouch!

Colorado jumped over the skid-board and grabbed the stone so that Mr. McFrey could get his hand out. Same hand as before! This time, seeing as how his fingers were already sore from before, he did a little Irish dance, while grabbing his hand and gave a very enthusiastic bow that he seemed not to be able to rise from.

The next day . . . Well . . . that blasted cast was just too big to put in his pocket!

Mr. McFrey would have never been on anyone's payroll for employee relations, as one can ascertain from what has already been said. With that, let there be no doubt that none of the employees had any respect or love for Mr. McFrey. Further evidence will indeed cement that opinion.

Big Ben, as some called him, had been asking Mr. McFrey for time off to see his new grandchild, since my grandfather had yielded all those decisions to Mr. McFrey. Ben asked if he could get off early on Friday afternoon so that he would have a weekend to see the grandchild.

Mr. McFrey refused, saying that he would actually like for him to work on Saturday. Of course Ben balked at the suggestion, sighting the fact that he had already worked the last six Saturdays consecutively without even a "thank you" from Mr. McFrey.

Of course Mr. McFrey told Ben that he was lying. My father, who was working on the other side of the office was about to intercede on Ben's behalf when Ben interceded on his own behalf.

"Mr. Jim, I've been pretty patient. I've always done what ya asked me."

"Hrmph," Mr. McFrey blurted. This took Ben to his limit.

"Mr. McFrey, sir, yous need to pay me for my Sattidys, and I need to get a half a day off Friday, or you's not gonna like what I do!"

"Oh yeah! What is you gonna do?" asked Mr. McFrey mockingly as he swung around in his swivel chair and leaned back defiantly.

Ben pulled out a gun and fired it toward Mr. McFrey's crotch—that's what he did about it! Fifty years later that bullet is still in that chair. From the looks of where that bullet is in that chair, Mr. McFrey raised up just enough to save his manhood.

It really was a different world back then. My father told Jim to forget about calling the police because he'll swear that he didn't see a thing. You see, my father didn't care a whole lot for Mr. McFrey since the entire reason he was a partner in the first place was because he had won a third of the company in a poker game.

My grandfather had actually lost his entire two-thirds, but played all night until he settled for getting half of that back. A couple of the other players swore that Jim had cheated on the very hand that lost Grand-dad his part in the first place.

Anyway, Ben kept his job, did not go to jail, and did get his half a day off and did get his overtime pay for his extra Saturday work, with a 15¢ an hour raise to boot. My father saw to it. My grandfather seconded it.

You might wonder why Mr. McFrey stayed at the job with very little support from his partners. Well . . . He was making too much money to quit and it took my father until after my grandfather retired to figure it out.

As long as my grandfather was working, my father had very little to do with the books. My grandfather was getting tired and was too busy going after new business, which unfortunately also included a little funny business (which he was getting a little too old to be doing in the first place) to pay too much attention to what Mr. McFrey was doing. This fact afforded Mr. McFrey the opportunity to cook the books, which he did on a regular basis. I think the proper term is "putting his hand in the cookie jar."

As soon as my father started looking at the checkbook on a regular basis, he noticed that the deposits never matched the volume of work that was being done in the shop. This prompted him to get a ledger book and write down every single sale that occurred. Would you believe that it took less than three months for Mr. McFrey to offer to sell his half of the company to my father?

If my father had been even slightly ruthless, he probably could have gotten the company for nothing. Nevertheless, he became the sole owner for not really a lot of money. Of course he and my mom were already afflicted with a house full of pitter-patter and hungry mouths. And so, as you know, my fate was sealed.

***

The Missing Link?

The fact is, to continue this narrative, it might be helpful if you knew a little bit about me so I might as well start at the beginning. Not the "beginning" beginning (that has already been established) but instead, my beginning. I only know my very beginning from a very reliable witness who happened to be there the exact second that I was born and that would be my mother, so I have every reason to believe her.

I was born during the height of Elvis Presley's early fame and probably during a round of golf by Dwight David Eisenhower. An entirely different Johnathan Kevin Sanders would have been born if my mother had not had a miscarriage a mere six weeks before I was conceived. Might this be a subject for the scholarly? Who knows? On top of that, who cares?

Ordinarily most stories are . . . ordinary. I suppose that my life for the most part is not extraordinary just as are most everyone's, but it has had its moments. The fact that my father and grandfather were in the tombstone business did, I believe at least, fashion a fairly unique life for me.

As I said I was born during Elvis's early popularity, which I mention in the first place because it places my birth in the 1950s. In the second place because all the nurses at the hospital who saw me said that I looked like Elvis. It was mainly due to my very thick mane and manly-looking sideburns. They all said that I was adorable in spite of the fact that I was also covered from head to toe with very black (though thin) hair.

My parents, however, were deeply disturbed. My mother, having to decide between feeding me and facing a guilty conscience, reluctantly threw away her anxieties and declared that I was a very sweet little primate and set about her task of assuring my survival. I somewhat believe that they thought of shaving me to prevent anyone from using me to promote their belief in evolution. In point of fact her father did call me a fat little monkey for the first ten years of my life.

My father, on the other hand, could not even look at me, and when relatives came to eye this precious little bundle, he pretended to be helping my mother with supper and, with a very jovial air, would try to send them upstairs alone. My mother, who should not have been cooking that soon after giving birth, would put down her utensils and carry the guests upstairs and proudly show me off in a barely lit room.

"Why are the lights so low in here? I can't even see the baby!" purportedly my grandmother said.

To which my mother replied that I was very sensitive to light and that the doctor had insisted that she keep the shades drawn and use no more than a fifteen-watt light bulb in the lamp. On top of that, my father had installed a dimmer switch so that all you would see was the bulb's barely glowing filament and not much else. (Of course, Mom would at least turn it up enough to keep from falling into my crib!)

My grandmother insisted that she needed a little more light and opened the curtains. She saw me as something other than some wretched little creature and took me in her arms and looked adoringly at her tenth grandchild.

Mother confessed to her at that moment that my father had not looked at me more than once since my leaving the hospital. At this revelation my grandmother reeled on her toes and swept me downstairs to confront my father.

Being that it was his mother that was confronting him, he took note of her demeanor and knew that it was hopeless to resist the expected tongue lashing that he was soon to receive. As a child he experienced her deadly accurate forehand on many occasions when he sassed her or even dared to look at her cross eyed and so he decided that he would obey all rules at this moment in order to keep his teeth. The better to eat his supper with!

"Norman, you should be ashamed of yourself for ignoring your tiny little son! He can't help that he was born this way . . . I've seen many babies that were just as hairy as this one. It will change. The hair will come out. You need to help your wife just as much with this one as your other two! Do you hear me?"

"Yeh . . . yeh . . . yes, ma'am," replied my father.

"Do you hear me?"

"I . . . yes, ma'am."

"Then why aren't you looking at him?"

It is a good thing that my father had not yet eaten or he might have wasted a perfectly delicious pot roast on the wallpaper. One miniscule cowardly glance and he would have been done for!

My father's father, on the other hand, stated plainly without reservation that I was the ugliest damn baby that he had ever seen in his life. In one respect that detail may have played a part in the fact that I was actually his favorite grandchild. I would just have to say to the rest of my family that you all should just get over it.

My grandmother was right! Two and a half weeks into my life, the hair did fall out. Even my super-luscious mane departed for the most part. I looked normal; that is to say that I looked like Winston Churchill. My father couldn't believe his eyes. My mother cried. So did my brother; he liked having a pet monkey for a brother!

Just because I looked normal didn't mean that I was. I did indeed act more like what my original covering implied. At the age of nineteen months (which was verified by my mother), I looked up at the ceiling of our carport and decided that I wanted to touch it. I was maybe two feet tall, the ceiling ten. There was no ladder, but there was a pole that, of course, kept the roof from crashing.

I didn't hesitate!

I climbed!

I reached the ceiling and I exaltedly touched it.

My mother was in the kitchen where I could just see her legs through the screen door. She was busy cooking supper so I knew that she couldn't see me.

"Hey, Mama!" I announced in my little baby voice. She ignored me I thought. "Hey Mama!" I announced again more loudly. I was beginning to feel dejected when suddenly she glided nonchalantly to the door. Seeing her, I started vigorously waving to her with one arm and holding on with the other with my legs wrapped around the pole.

"Hello, son," she said indifferently as she looked up at me with what I thought was a somewhat dismissive air.

"You need to come down soon," she said. "We're going to eat supper as soon as your daddy gets home."

"Okay, Mama."

She turned slowly to go back to her cooking and did not wish to see my descent, owing to the fact that she also did not wish to see my demise. (She confessed years later that she was scared witless.)

I thought that what I had done was just an everyday sort of thing. So I shinnied on down with my bare little legs and arms slightly sticking and screeching all of the way. I ran into the house, the screen door "screech-cluhbanged" behind me.

"Did you see me?" I asked excitedly.

"Yes, son," she replied with a slightly higher voice than before.

I was waiting for praise. Mother kept cooking.

"I climbed up there!" I pointed.

"Yes, you did!" she said as she smiled. She put down her utensil—I can still hear its clank— and gave me a hug. I felt her rapidly beating heart and didn't understand why.

For several years after, I occasioned many times for my mother's heart to race. I climbed everything. When I was still small enough I would climb atop the refrigerator to enter the cabinet above it so that I could surprise her as she was cooking supper. I stopped doing that when I was waylaid by a bag of flour.

Dad, brother, and sister came running into the kitchen thinking that my mom had caught the place on fire. I think that they were a little surprised that it looked like my mother was about to put me in the oven since I was good and powdered. By the time that I was three and a half I took up too much space in the cabinets anyway.

When I was four, with great intensity I watched our neighbor build a fence from four-by-four posts, some hog wire, which is of heavy gauge wire that crisscrosses in a perpendicular fashion to create neat little "ladders" for little boys to stick their feet in and climb. Near the top and bottom of each post were two-by-four rails that connected them all of the way around the yard, which amounted to about three hundred and eighty feet.

When Mr. Langston finished the fence, after three days of hard work, he went inside for a break and had not been through for more than half an hour when I walked over to it and stuck my little foot in one of the "rungs" to test it out. I didn't hesitate. I climbed! I reached the two by four and stood up on it. It felt steady. I was ready.

I was approximately thirty feet from the right hand corner closest to both houses. That was too short of a distance to excite me and there was a gate close to the house that I couldn't get over anyway. I looked to my left. Ah! "That's a nice long way so I think I will go that way!"

Did I think about my mother? My father? Brother? Sister? Grandmother, dog, cat, or even Jesus? Shoot no! I just watched my feet and the two-by-four and the four-by-four posts when I reached them. At first I was a little timid, but by the time that I had traversed the halfway point, I picked up the pace and scooted on around to the other side of their house and touched the brick wall.

I remember peering into the bedroom window and being surprised and disappointed that no one was there to greet me. So I turned around and went back. Once I got around to where I could see my mother through the kitchen window at the back of the house I started waving. She was peeling potatoes, I guess, and didn't see me at first, so I looked back down at my feet and continued on.

After twenty or so feet, I looked back at the window and saw Mother staring at me with her mouth slightly ajar. Of course I just smiled and waved and shouted, "Look, Mama. Look what I'm doing!"

"I see that, son. You be careful."

How many times did I hear that? Six thousand! Almost as many times as I heard "I'm going to whip your tail!" When I was little I never understood why she would say that, when my big brother had assured me that they cut mine off just after I was born.

"I went all the way around and touched the house!"

"That's nice, but don't you fall!"

"I won't." There it was. The first inkling of doubt! It never occurred to me that I could fall. What made her doubt me? The mood that she had initiated in me didn't last long so I just kept walking.

I walked all the way back to the gate but saw that I couldn't get past it to touch the house on this side, so I turned around and went back around and this time I saw Mr. Langston walking out of the bedroom. I turned around again and made it twenty to thirty feet by the time that I saw him standing in the back yard with his hands on his hips.

At first I thought that I was in trouble, but soon realized that he was smiling and heard him say, "Boy! What in thunder are you doing?"

"Nothing," I shrugged. "I'm just walking."

"Now you come on down from there before you hurt yourself," he said in a gentle but firm voice.

There it was again! Doubt. Twice in twenty minutes! I didn't get down right away; I walked all the way back to where I had started and semi-defiantly climbed down. I knew that I was safe the whole time. But in time I did find out that doubt has its place.

Doubt has its place, but many of us place it on a gilded throne that rules our every move. As with any small child, I suppose, grownup's warnings to me sounded no more than the chatter of a distressed squirrel. How doubts do sidle into our psyche at the most inopportune times! Where did yours come from?

Time and again I continued my quest for greater and more difficult heights! At four and a half I started climbing trees. Small trees at first, the ones that I could reach the limbs from the ground. "That tree, there! The one closest to the street . . . That limb there, I can't reach it . . . I'll wrap my arms and legs around it . . . It's too big! There's my brother's bicycle . . . I'll get it and push it over to the tree . . . I'll climb up on the bike . . . I'll stand on the seat . . . I can't reeeeeeach the limb . . . I'll streeeeeeeeatch out as farrrrrr as I cannnn . . . I got it . . . got to hold as tight as I can . . . I'll pull up with my arms . . . then pull my knees up and clamp down . . . I'll pull some more with my arms . . . clamp down . . . pull up . . . most of me is above the limb . . . I can reach the next limb! I've made it! I can keep going! I'm at the top! Oooo! This tree is moving back and forth really far! Hey! There's Mama! "HEY MAMA!"

"Hey, son! Where are you? I can't see you."

"I'm up here!"

"Where? I still can't see you!"

"Up here!" I said in an altogether giggly little voice.

Then she saw me. Forty feet up! Sitting in the last little fork in the tree. I think this might have been when I really began to read body language. She was walking and yet she seemed to be paralyzed at the same time. It was more like she was being carried on a conveyor, or perhaps the earth was moving and she was standing still. She came out to get the mail and walked on to the mailbox no longer looking up. After retrieving the mail, she slowly walked back to the house and ever so slightly turned her head and said (you guessed it) "Beeeeee careful!"

Now you might think that she should have paid more attention to me in the first place, but every day she actually did call out to me every ten to fifteen minutes to see where I was. In all fairness too, a few months before, she added a fourth child to her collection.

As you might have figured by now, I got down okay from that climb and many others without fatally falling for I am definitely narrating this tale from neither Heaven nor Hell.

They say that God looks after children and fools. But does He look after foolish little children? He must—in my case, at least. So I continued to test the "survival of the fittest" platitude until I grew and went to school and discovered that in the modern world, surviving public school unaltered is akin to surviving a nuclear blast. In other words, you may try to stay as far away from ground zero as possible, but that target just keeps on a moving.

***

Don't Make Me Go!

When I was growing up, I lived in the largest single suburb of the city. It was called Garden Lakes, which confused me somewhat because, even though I could see lots of lakes, I never saw any gardens that stood on the same level, so to speak, as the lakes.

My brother informed me with his typical sarcasm that it was named such because it was a garden of lakes.

Then why didn't they name it "Garden of Lakes," I questioned.

My mother said it was because it would have been too easy for strangers to think that we were saying Gardenia Lakes or Garnolakes or such because so many people from our area had lazy tongues.

Our mother really worked on our enunciation, which made the locals think that we were from somewhere else. I was often asked where was I born and I surprised people with my answer. I was born right here!

Here is where I entered school. At the time, kindergarten was optional and had to be paid for out of pocket. My father's pockets were not very deep so as far as my option went for attending kindergarten it was a mandatory no. So primarily I entered the first grade a year behind most of my peers.

A few days before school started, while I was in the backyard swinging away on my swing set, I told my mother, who was looking out of the kitchen window as usual, that I wasn't going to school.

"Oh yes, you are!"

"Oh no, I'm not!"

"Oh! And why aren't you going to school?"

"Because I don't want to, because I can't read or write."

"Well, silly, that is why you are going to school, so that you can learn to read and write! Besides, you'll also get to color and paste and you'll get to play outside for recess and meet a lot of new children."

"I already know how to color and play outside and Celina can teach me how to read and write and I already know some children."

"I don't have time to argue with you right now. I have to fix supper."

On top of that she was only three and half months away from adding number five to her collection. Suffice it to say that she was in no mood to do anything except maybe murder my father.

Well, anyway we had to prepare for school and I was not happy. We went to the school to register my sister for third grade and of course me for first.

Mother—carrying my little brother on her hip, my little sister in her tummy, holding my hand, and directing my older sister—led the way into the school.

The first things that struck me were the smells of cleaning solution and the new paint on the walls. I was immediately intimidated by the long two-tone claustrophobic walls that at first appeared to have no end. I had not seen any other details including doors, the principal's office, the lunch room, nor the fact that we had made several turns to get to my sister's room of registration.

As always, whenever we went anywhere, my mother would see someone she knew and of course she did this time too. She took a registration card from this lady sitting behind a desk and walked over to Bette and sat down at a desk next to her. Conversation was no stranger to my mother so while filling out the card, she conversed . . . and conversed.

I was so taken by the little blonde-headed girl that I had not noticed that my mother was no longer conversing. I had only noticed that Bette had looked down and was filling out her card and was no longer nodding and smiling at my mother.

My pineal gland told me to turn around and I found myself without my mother, sister, brother, and the bun in the oven! That was the second time that I had felt real panic. I ran through the halls and out a door and in through another door and down another hall and around and around until I wound up outside right where we had started.

I looked out to the parking lot and could not see our car. I looked back at the school and saw no evidence of any satisfactory outcome. My mother went home without me! Wait! She forgot to register me! Maybe I'm safe. I don't have to go to school!

"I'll walk home and hide in the woods until she forgets this nonsense."

I started home and heard, "Kevin, honey, where are you going?" Now of course she called me "honey" because she had witnesses and would have given me the old "what for" if she hadn't. I always liked witnesses; they seemed to make my mother a very happy and caring person.

I was relieved and disappointed at the same time so I lowered my head and trundled on to my mother who took me in to register me. School hadn't even started and already I had been dealt a dose of bitter fate. Yikes!

We found my room of registration and this time I took a close account of everything around me, including the water fountain to the immediate left of the door. I took a mental picture of every single thing in that room as we entered. I did not take my eyes off Mother. Every move, every twitch, every breath was stored in my brain. I was not getting left behind any more.

So we finished our duty and out we went. I counted every single tile that I tread upon (I could only count to a hundred so I started over quite a few times!). I counted every door in the hallway. I noticed chips and cracks in the concrete blocks. I was not going to get lost ever again.

As we returned home I looked out at the big lake and marveled at its shimmer in the late summer sun. I imagined each tiny reflection as one of a million brightly illuminated creatures dancing mindlessly, cheerfully, with no idea of impending doom, on the ruffled surface.

I saw myself dancing atop the gentle waves and smiling carelessly, with my eyes closed tightly, facing the sun and holding hands with one of them. "Alas," I told them "I must leave you now, but I will see you tomorrow to tell you good-bye because I must run away."

"Then you must tell us now because tomorrow might be cloudy and we won't be here."

Even at not quite six years old I saw the gloom of an uncertain future. So I sighed and brought my imagination to a halt and stared out at the front of our Edsel and began my plan of escape.

I decided that I should go ahead and leave that day but waited until midafternoon. I had eaten a very big lunch because I wasn't sure when I would next eat. I figured on running away to at least as far as the little grocery store, which was a mile away, because I knew there was food there and a hammock out back tied between two trees. I remembered seeing a garden hose that had been cut down to a few feet, so I would have water.

So there it was. But I couldn't leave without saying good-bye to my mother. I went to the screen door of the kitchen and saw her ironing. I hesitated, not because I was changing my mind, but because she might stop me.

My fear was allayed when she didn't even look at me when I told her.

"Hey, Mama, I'm going to run away."

"Okay, son."

"I'm leaving."

"Change your underwear first."

"Okay. Well . . . 'bye."

I heard the steam venting from the iron and took that as an okay. I headed for the woods that adjoined our property and hit the trail that was created by a bulldozer as a fire break, which ran parallel to our street. At a half mile it ended at a drainage ditch that came from the little lake.

I figured that when I got to the ditch that I could turn to the right and get onto our street and make my way to the store. As I was running (one actually runs, I also figured, when one runs away), I was absolutely delirious with joy. Just as I had gotten to the ditch and was about to jump, I felt a strong pull from a familiar hand. Oh no! It was Big Brother.

"Where do you think you are going?" he asked sharply.

"I'm running away," I replied matter-of-factly. *How did he catch me?* I thought. I was running as fast as I could!

"No, I think you better come home. Mom is going to be really mad."

"Well, she said I could!"

"I'll betcha she didn't either."

"She did! She said 'okay'!"

With that he popped me on the head and grabbed my shirt and steered me toward the house. I finally quit resisting and began to doubt what I had done. It wasn't just because I knew that my buns were about to be toasted, but that I might also have befallen a certain calamity if I had succeeded with my folly.

When we re-entered our yard, I looked up and saw my mother standing there with her arms folded with a very dangerous-looking "hickry" sticking out of one of her fisted hands. That is what we called any sort of torture device that resembled a switch.

Our switches were usually made from a privet bush that, I swear to you, is still there. It could be an offspring, but it is possible that its growth was stunted by the perpetual "pruning" by my brothers and me. Most days we had to get our own torture device and it had better pass the hikry code or Mom would go out and get one that looked like a stick of lumber to me. Well, she had one that definitely surpassed the code that might as well have been listed in the "No Child Left with a Behind" code book!

I had no idea that that little pregnant lady could move so fast! Boom, she was on me. She grabbed my wrist, and around and around we went doing the "hikry dance." You have to run as fast as you can but you have to kick your legs forward at the same time to mark time to the "music" of the swishing hikry to lessen the blow as much as you can. You couldn't get away from it anyway because most mothers could break the sound barrier once they got cranked up, and my mother was the Zen master of hikry swishing. A lot of the neighborhood mothers would come to my mother for advice for the most effective techniques!

Ultimately you have to wear down your "partner" enough that they finally give out. My mother, however, was so well conditioned from her many dances that she proved to have prolific stamina. All the while she's swishing she's lecturing.

"You know that you could get hurt or killed!"

You mean sort of like what's going on now, I thought.

"Just wait until your father gets home!"

I wish he would hurry up so he could stop this craziness, I also thought.

"Are you ever going to do that again?"

"Wah wah wah wah!"

"Well, are you?"

"No, ma'am!" Sob, sob.

If I hadn't said "ma'am," I would have gotten at least ten more swishes, so as you can see I was learning very quickly how to be a very polite little boy.

It suddenly stopped and frankly once it had gone on a little while I didn't really feel it. So, after all of that, I realized that running away was futile and school might not be so bad after all.

***

The Gates of Hell

Here it was. My first day of school. My older brother and sister left home on foot, but my mother decided that for my first day she would drive me. I had the sense that we were running a little behind, but knew not to say anything.

Even though it was an average late summer day, my mother decided to dress me instead of allowing me to do it. I had been dressing myself since I was three, but this particular day she wanted to make sure that I was especially tidy and that I would wear my best non-church clothes.

I wore khaki shorts with a white button up shirt and a navy blue Izod sweater. I wore brown lace up shoes and white cotton sox. She licked her fingers and tried to paste down my cow lick. She gave me a hug and directed me to go get into the car.

Still the clock ticked while I waited for her to come out, but I heard the phone ring. It was her mother, who called her every morning, wanting to know if all of us had gotten to school okay.

Mother, after several minutes, finally told her that she had to go. So out she came with little brother in tow and practically jumped into the car and started it, slamming it in to reverse and backing out into the street. She slammed it into forward and pealed rubber. She flew down the road and around the lake. I noticed that there were no other children on the road, but thought maybe the walkers had to get to school really early.

When we entered the school grounds, Mother slowed to the proper speed. She always wanted to look and be proper. I noticed that no other children were outside so I was a little timid to walk up to the doors by myself.

I looked at Mother with pleading eyes, but she had already told me that she would simply pull up to the front and let me out.

"You have a good day, son! I know that you're going to come home and tell me all about your new friends and how excited you are to get to learn new things!"

"Mom, couldn't you at least take me just inside!?"

"NO! You go on in. You will be okay. I love you."

I just turned and with my head and shoulders drooping, walked slowly up to the double doors. I pulled on the handles, but they were locked! I turned around to get assistance from my mother, but she was gone! I walked out far enough from the front entrance to see into a classroom but couldn't tell if anyone noticed me.

I walked back under the large roof that jutted out over the walkway from the entrance and sat down. I was in a real panic and was just about to cry when a very nice man, whom I remembered as being the principal who wore a light yellow shirt and striped tie, opened the doors and asked me if I was there to go to school.

I stood up and replied that I was, so he came out and gently placed his hand on the back of my head and led me in.

When we got to the front hall, he asked me if I knew where to go.

"Yes, sir," I was afraid to say otherwise so I replied in the most timid little voice that one had ever heard coming from my mouth.

"Are you in the first grade?"

"Yes, sir, I think so."

"Okay, then yours is the next hall so let's go on down here. Now you just go on down there until you find your room." He motioned as he bent slightly. "Your name will be on a piece of paper with all of the other kids next to your room."

He patted me on the back and gave me a gentle nudge.

I nodded and walked slowly away from him wondering why he couldn't simply walk me to my room. I remembered my room of registration and figured that that was where I needed to go. I got to the door and saw the list of names, but hell! I couldn't read! Evidently all of the other kids could, so I figured that I would just fake it and walk on in.

There was only one vacant desk that was at the back of the classroom near the door. I noticed that the teacher had stopped talking and looked squarely at me. I knew then that I was really late. I nervously sat down and waited for her to speak to me, but she merely nodded to me and quietly left the room.

All of the children turned and stared at me, but said nothing. I wondered if by being late that I was in mortal danger. I thought for sure I was going to get the blame and that my mother would spank me to save face.

After a very short time, the teacher returned with another lady who looked directly at me and spoke.

"Kevin?"

"Yes, ma'am." How in heck did she know my name?

She beckoned for me with her index finger to follow her, so I embarrassedly got up and obediently followed her to my appropriate room. I really didn't like where all this was going and felt like this was only the beginning.

Recess came none too soon. We were instructed to leave the room in single file, yet once we were outside, all hell broke loose and children scattered everywhere except me! I stood under a large pine tree alone until another timid little boy walked up to me and asked my name. After exchanging names, he ran off before I could even ask him if he wanted to play.

I sighed and continued to stand there until another larger boy came up to me and said that I was standing under his tree. I walked away and was headed toward the swings but saw that all were occupied. I had only been standing there waiting for a turn when another boy came up to me and shoved me backward, very hard over the back of another boy, who had snuck up behind me and gone down on all fours.

They were both wearing miniature army uniforms, including the same kind of caps that Fidel Castro wore and shouted, "We're in the second grade and you'll do what we say!"

I had landed quiet hard and was aching badly when suddenly my bladder had filled to an excruciating level so I ran toward the door and was stopped by my teacher.

"Whoa! Where do you think you're going?"

"I've got to go bad!" I pleaded as I did the cross-legged pee dance.

"Oh no. You should have gone when we had bathroom break."

"I didn't have to go then . . . I have to go now!"

"You still had your chance. I'm not letting you in," she said coldly.

Okay, so what do you think happened? Correct! I peed in my pants. It was fortunate for me that first graders were let out early for the first six weeks of school or I would have had to sit for three and a half hours in soggy pants that didn't smell so nice either.

What was already a very slow day to me slowed even more. I was in a real conundrum. The teacher should have called my mother, but on the other hand I was sure to get the blame.

And of course I got the blame, but that was all. I didn't get the hikry and so that was the silver lining to what was a very stormy first day of school for a not-quite-six-year-old boy.

***

The Reason Ritalon Is
Not Always a Bad Idea

I was very close in age to a passel of boys on our street and played with all of them often. There were two sets of brothers that I divided time between the most, when we weren't all playing football or baseball together.

Jack and Bobby were more enthusiastic when it came to adventurous things than the Grogan brothers, so one day they came to my house to go for a hike, which was one of my favorite things.

Bobby was like Ernest T. Bass on the *Andy Griffith Show* and the Tasmanian devil on the *"Bugs Bunny"* cartoons.

Jack was a big lummox with dry skin, whom Tommy Clemmons would point out to everyone as loud as he could, "Ah hell, there's Jack snowing again."

Everyone would laugh but me, and that's why poor Jack considered me his best friend. It was difficult, because you really could see his skin flaking off him like tiny little snowflakes dancing in the breeze. It was so gross to me that I couldn't laugh.

Since I lived right in front of the largest single college campus on earth, which at the time was many thousands of acres, my house was the perfect starting point for any hike.

Behind our house, there was an old jeep trail that led to another set of trails that led to an old WPA road that was access to some of the logging that went on on campus. In those days all the logging was select cut with none of the inherent destruction that goes on today.

When groups of trees were felled, they were dragged to a convenient spot and sawn to suitable lengths. These were very old pines that were used for buildings, including many of the ones on campus, which created huge piles of sawdust.

Huge piles of sawdust are very tempting to eight and nine year old boys so I took the Dempsey brothers and my cousin Mel, who was seven, to see the miracle of modern engineering. So off we went.

I had told them all that I would show them something that they would marvel over, probably the rest of their lives. They said I was full of baloney, and that's exactly what they said. We didn't use profanity like kids do now.

Bobby, who was eight, asked me if it was a German tank. We were kids. We didn't know geography, except Jack who knew everything. No, I said it was better than that.

"I bet it's a plane crash then!" enthused Bobby.

"No," I said. "It's even better. You'll see, we're almost there."

Mel was quiet; he was just glad to be there. Jack, being a big lummox, was winded so he took up the rear while saying that since he was the biggest he could watch out for us better from there.

I knew the real reason that Jack took up the rear was because he couldn't keep up, because he never could keep up, but I was perfectly happy that he was behind so that I didn't have to hear his horrifically laborious breathing.

Because he was an exact clone of Ernest T. Bass, Bobby talked all the way, sounding like a hoard of seventeen year locusts. When we reached the creek, which was half way through our journey, Bobby plowed right through and got thoroughly soaked. The rest of us decided to jump. We found the narrowest place to jump. Well, to us it looked wide even there, but in reality it was only three or four feet. I went first and surprised myself when I made it with ease. Jack helped boost Mel across so he made it fine. Jack took his best "lummoxion" shot and landed with one foot in the water and stumbled and fell onto the bank.

With his reddened face and snot pouring from his nose, Jack got up without saying a word, because he knew that if he did, we would jump on any excuse like a pack of jackals and rip his proverbial heart out, but because he didn't speak, we simply turned toward our destination and continued our journey.

Of course Bobby cut loose with his shriekish laughter that would have chilled a banshee. We were used to it, but no one else in our neighborhood was. I've seen a gaggle of frightened mothers stop right in the middle of an uproarious conversation, all with the look of mortal fright on their faces when they would hear Bobby laughing a block away.

Just as my companions were about to get discouraged, we hit the WPA road. It was a beautiful spring day, and all along the road and back through the woods, on the other side, the dogwoods were in full bloom, giving the impression that it had snowed the night before.

The day was still young so the sun was filtering through the foliage of the very tall pines, casting thousands of shadows through the golden mist that was pure magic to our young souls. The air felt as though it had been scrubbed clean with baking soda and all that was heard was the wind, the birds, the blood pounding in our ears, and the sound of our own breathing.

The scent of pine and sassafras sent a rush through me that heightened my excitement for our destination. The golden hue of the road of yellow clay, which is as prevalent in our area as the legendary Georgia red clay, reminded me of my mother's promise that the roads of Heaven are paved with gold.

I'm sure it left its mark on Bobby, for even he was still for a moment.

Alas, the spell was broken by "Ernest T. Devil," so we went on our way to my equivalent of Disneyland.

I knew we were very near to our destination when I saw the ruts from the heavy equipment that they had made while piling the sawdust, leaving two perpetual elliptical pools of murky water.

You couldn't see the sawdust pile just yet because it was tucked away just off the road and was hidden by the tree line. Another hundred yards and it would be visible and I was getting even more excited while the rest were getting restless.

Mel, who had been glad just for being allowed to come, began to fret and whined that he wanted to go back. Jack said that he thought we were lost and agreed with Mel that we should go back.

Bobby laughed his laugh, and because he took advantage of every opportunity to accost Jack, said that he would take a stick to Jack's head if he did go back. With that he picked up a six-foot oak branch and started chasing him down the road toward the sawdust pile.

Even though Bobby was handicapped by branch, Jack was handicapped by "klutzation," so their locomotion was fairly equal and just as Bobby was about to clobber Jack they stopped, spellbound by what was now before them.

Because Mel and I were running unimpeded we caught up quickly and reached the Dempsey brothers looking at the massive mound with their jaws agape.

Mel too was astonished, and even though I tried to be cool, I'm sure I was grinning wide enough to swallow a football. You have to understand, we were little boys, five miles from home, on foot, and without adults, and . . . uh . . . without permission.

The sawdust pile was ultra magnificent to our puerile eyes as it beckoned to us to commit an all-out assault on its daunting height. In reality the pile was probably only fifteen feet, but we told our friends at school that it was thirty.

We ran to the top, or rather we slogged our way to the top, and after the five miles to our destination, we were pretty tired. So we sat down, not caring that an inch below the surface, the sawdust was wet from the spring rain which soaked us clean through to our underwear. This created a nice patina of the soggy shavings all over our pants, but to each of us it was a reward much better than a dollar for straight As.

Jack and I carried WWII surplus knapsacks packed with baloney sandwiches and potato chips, so we settled down for a while to eat. Each of us had our own supply of water, carried in WWII surplus canteens, which tasted entirely like the aluminum in which it was residing.

We communed nicely for a while until Bobby dropped his half eaten sandwich, which he picked up and held to Jack's mouth. Jack clinched his lips and did nothing more to resist Bobby than to keep leaning away from him until he fell over backward and slid head first on his back down the other side.

Mel and I did little more than look over our shoulders, observing the much distressed Jack sliding to within inches of a tangle of blackberry bushes, and went back to our sandwiches and metallic water.

Bobby trundled down the sloppy slope and helped Joe recover his proper orientation, but it was merely a brief interlude until the next fracas. What followed next appeared rather strange to Jack, Mel, and me.

As Jack was trying to gather himself and clean the sticky pulp from his neck and ears and the waist of his pants, Bobby began to burrow his way into the sawdust pile like a four foot four–inch hairless rodent.

He went in over the length of his body, not caving in the mass at all. Jack forgot his grief and looked at me with wide eyes. Jack and I had the simultaneous notion that we could tunnel our way all the way through to the other side.

So the two of us reached into Bobby's shallow tunnel and both of us grabbed one of his feet and pulled him out. We told him of our inspiration to which he replied without speaking but instead laughed with an "Igor" kind of laugh, which made his shoulders bob up and down. Having been together our whole life, we knew that he too was inspired.

Since we were all intelligent boys, we decided not to start the tunnel at the bottom because it was way too wide and we knew that it would take way too long to traverse its seventy foot diameter.

After several minutes, maybe even two, we decided the order that we would proceed. Jack didn't want to go first, and he didn't want Bobby to be directly in front or behind him or go first because there was no telling where he would lead us, so I was elected to go first, Jack second, Mel third, and the frenetic one last.

Whenever Bobby was involved, there was no such thing as a logically foolproof plan. But it was what it was

Jack pulled out his authentic WWII multi-purpose shovel that his dad actually used during the war in Europe and handed it to me.

I remember thinking that Bobby hadn't needed a shovel but I took it anyway.

It was easy starting, but it got tougher as we got deeper into the more tightly packed interior.

When I got in far enough Jack followed so that he could remove what I couldn't by facing my rear and pushing the debris between his legs, and then Mel entered and repeated the process, and then of course madman Bobby was last. Bobby would take what we passed to him and remove it from the tunnel very quickly, much like an over energized hamster.

Our little conveyer was working well, but I must have turned toward the less dense outer ring and wound up bringing us out higher and too much to the left than we intended so we were dismayed but not too discouraged that our tunnel was short.

We climbed down and started over in the original opening, but this time I was so determined to stay in the center that I veered too far to the right.

Unknowingly I was circumventing the mound and because of the increased distance was growing tired so I convinced the others to back out to take a break and gather our strength.

When we backed out, we could tell that we were making an arc, so Joe suggested that we turn slightly to the right so that we could exit earlier than what we had expected.

As you can guess, the deeper we went the darker it got, but when I looked back with great difficulty, I could see light behind the silhouettes of the others so I instinctively knew that we were going in a straight line.

Suddenly, there was no light at all, which gave Jack, Mel, and me a fright, but it didn't bother Bobby.

I thought that I heard laughter coming from the outside but thought that it was my imagination until I heard Jack call out to Bobby and then heard no reply!

Bobby had backed out of the tunnel and climbed up over it and began to dance which left Mel in the rear to inadvertently plug the hole because there was no one there to clear it.

Mel couldn't turn around to dig out toward the entrance because the tunnel was too narrow, and so Jack and I became extremely "adrenalised" and dug with great ferocity.

We were closer to the end than we had thought and broke through within minutes only to find that we were facing a massive entanglement of the aforementioned blackberries.

We had also been closer to the surface than we thought because Bobby's dancing caused the tunnel to cave in.

We felt it giving in so we clambered toward the blackberries knowing that having cuts and scratches were better than taking the eternal dirt nap in a coffin! I barely got my head out when it collapsed, but Jack and Mel were too far back to get anything out.

I was pretty worried by this point; I just knew that the other two were going to die. I heard Bobby making a strange noise like an exultant chimpanzee and thought that he was flipping out, but in reality, what he was doing was digging the others out.

Bobby got Mel uncovered enough so that he could work the rest of his own way out, but only uncovered Jack enough so that he could breathe. Jesus wept . . . Bobby laughed!

Somehow in the fray I was able to free one arm, which then freed the other. At first I didn't realize that my face was stuck in the blackberries, but learned *mucho pronto* that it was when I tried to disengage myself from the sawdust pile.

I believe that this experience was the catalyst in my supposition that pain was the most convincing statement that lets you know that you are alive. I still say "be glad for pain," even though people look askance at me when I say it.

Jack started to cry out like an old hound dog, which infuriated me enough that I was able to get up and wade through the now-loosened sawdust and bitch-slap him right across the face. It might have been cruel, but it did shut him up.

I went after Bobby next and was going to separate him from his soul one way or the other, but unfortunately, he took flight, shall we say! He headed toward the mountain as fast as he could and left our sight in a matter of minutes.

After Mel and I freed Jack, I apologized to him for slapping him, which he humbly accepted and he began to sob. Mel was perplexed that I hadn't comforted him, because he too was buried alive, but then I explained to him that he hadn't lived with the Tasmanian devil for eight years and one month.

Miraculously we found the shovel and everything else, so we gathered it all up and headed for home, not giving a rat's hind quarter what might happen to Bobby.

Jack sobbed all the way home, dropping tears so large that you could hear them hitting the dried leaves on the ground.

We expected Bobby to get home way after we would, seeing that he took off in the wrong direction and had to traverse his way through many briar patches, but when we got back to their house, much to our irritation, we found him in the tree house, sitting on one leg, triumphantly swinging the other off the side, and eating a peanut butter and jelly sandwich.

Without saying a word, Jack went into the house and came back out with his BB gun and popped Bobby in the forehead, which caused him to drop his sandwich and lose his balance and fall from the tree house.

The fall wasn't that big of a deal since he landed in the pile of hay that they kept there just to jump in anyway.

Whatever . . . the fact that Jack took desperate measures to defend his honor, for the first time, was enough to make Bobby leave him alone from then on.

It didn't cure him . . .

***

"Dad gum it Bobby, throw me the ball! Where are you going? Come back here!"

"Get off of my back! What are you doing?"

That was Bobby. Every time we played basketball the game would be going just fine, and if he was on my team and we were about to win with one more bucket, he would either jump on my back just as I was about to make the winning shot or he would take off with the ball.

Sometimes Bobby would jump on me and have his arms and legs wrapped around me so tightly that I couldn't get them loose without leaning way back and taking him to the ground and forcing my butt into his gut causing the wind to blow out of him like a great whale. That was the only way that Jack's side ever won so he was always in a good mood whenever Bobby pulled his antics.

The boy was in desperate need of therapy, and because he never got any, everyone around him needed it too. The only other thing to do was just suck it up and put him out of your mind as soon as you got away from him.

Whenever we played baseball and he got a base hit, he would run toward third base instead of first and run all the way around back to home with Jack following him and screaming, "You're out, you're out, you're out!"

Bobby didn't care; he just bellowed his banshee-frightening laugh and kept on running. Sometimes he would pick up the bases as he went and would run off toward the lake. Geez, wish I was kidding.

Once, when he was still too young to drive a car, his dad bought him and Jack each one of those little Honda motorcycles that looked like something the Shriners clowns would ride around.

Their dad had only given them permission to ride around the lake, which Jack obediently did. But Bobby? Oh hell no!

Bobby was constantly getting in trouble on that little bike! Once he tried to pass this lady on the right side just as she was turning into her driveway. I remember the ambulance flying past our house . . . Police chases! Neighborhood dads throwing sticks and rocks at him!

One day the police chased him for a solid forty-five minutes until he lost them by turning down into the ditch (which was dry) that circled the lake where they couldn't see him and then he drove on to his house where he rapidly pulled into the garage, slammed the door shut, ran into his bedroom and jumped on his bed with a copy of popular science.

Jack, who shared the room with Bobby, was sitting at the desk and without turning around asked, "Are those cops out chasing *you?*"

Bobby just laughed. He didn't laugh when his dad took the bike away from him and disassembled it! Didn't matter to Bobby though; he gathered all the pieces and put it back together and would get so good at it after a while that he would disassemble it again before his father would get home.

When Bobby was sixteen and had his driver's license he got a job at a motorcycle dealership. The motorcycles arrived in crates partially disassembled. Bobby took one out of the crate and had it assembled faster than anyone in the history of motorcycle assembly.

The owner knew that he was hiring a real demon, partially because of the laugh and the snot blowing out his nose!

He bragged about going down the two-lane highway at 120 mph toward our high school, right in the middle of the center line! Cars going in both directions!

I called him a liar until one day, as I was heading to school, he roared past me at such a terrific rate of speed that it shook my car. I just knew that my father was going to have to make a visit to Mr. Dempsey to sell him a tombstone. Not to worry though, a stone was not to be placed at his head just yet.

I was the opposite. One day I was going a little too fast in my car heading toward my house when I encountered a policeman who was going the other way. I quickly turned down a side street before the policeman could get turned around, but instead of driving very fast I drove very very slowly.

I knew the neighborhood better than the policeman did and I kept turning down different side streets, but a block over, the policeman, who had never turned on his siren, would see me and turn toward me and I would turn down another street, but he always seemed to spy me wherever I went. It was the slowest speed chase in the history of police chases!

When I was just about to the spot where he spied me in the first place, I pulled over and stopped and waited for him. In about two minutes he came pulling up behind me. When he got out of the car, he walked up to me very slowly and asked for my license.

When I handed it to him, he told me that it was a good thing that I had pulled over and waited for him. He asked me how fast I was going.

"I don't know," I lied as I was staring at my speedometer.

"Yes, you do," he said matter-of-factly. "You know exactly how fast you were going! If you don't tell me the truth, I'm going to throw the book at you."

"Forty-two," I lied again because the fact is I was doing fifty-two.

"That's right," he said. "That's exactly what I clocked you at. If you had lied to me, I would have followed you to your house and given you a ticket in front of your parents and I bet they'd take that car away from you. Do you know what the speed limit is here?"

"Yes, sir . . . It's twenty-five."

"Then why were you going forty-two?"

"I don't know."

"Yes, you do. You know why you were going too fast."

"Yes, sir . . . It's because I'm stupid."

I saw the officer give a slight snicker and then he said, "*That's* a good answer. I'm not going to have to tell your parents and I'm going to let you off with a warning this time, but if I catch you again, I'm going to give you a ticket and I'll probably throw in a few more infractions to boot. Do you understand me?"

"Yes, sir . . . Thank you."

That was all I could say. I was not a great gambler ever because of that event, which is why it still puzzles me to this day as to how, years later, Bobby and I would launch one of the most harebrained schemes that two people of such diametrically opposed personalities could ever come up with.

***

Beyond the Gates of Hell

The first day of school was only more memorable than most of the rest of my school life just because it was the first day. My attitudes were definitely determined by my early years of school. It wasn't the school itself per se. It was the gd m f ing */;><*&Y*Y*(***/^%&%^&^$&^^%** other kids.

If you are young, you might think because your parents have lied to you all of your life that gd m f ing */;><*&Y*Y*(***/^%&%^&^$&^^%** kids are relatively new, but they're not. So how long have kids been gd m f ing */;><*&Y*Y*(***/^%&%^&^$&^^%** kids? How long has the human race been making kids? Well, then you know, don't you?

When I first started school, I was pretty much like every other little kid. When we were six years old, we were all pretty naïve and scared of our parents who also warned us that we should be scared of our teachers. We were told that if the teacher had to punish us for misbehaving, then we would have it twice as bad when we got home. Most everyone sat compliantly in their seat and listened to the teacher and didn't disrupt the class because if we didn't comply we knew we would get our hides tanned.

Recess, on the other hand, was more like a Darwinian experiment, mainly because the teachers really didn't pay any attention to us when we were outside. The real problem was that some of the older kids had recess at the same time that the little kids did. Second graders picked on first graders, third graders picked on second graders, and so on and so forth all the way up to eighth graders picking on seventh graders.

The fact that my father was in the monument business did not make a lot of difference to the kids in the first grade, because as you know, when we are little we don't care a whole lot about anything. What a difference a couple of years of the corruptive nature of public school makes!

When I was in the third grade, we had music class once a week. All of our county schools had the same music teacher who alternated from school to school. One day he delighted us with songs that he improvised using what our parents did for a living.

The teacher would pick out different children and ask them what their mother or father did; back then it was mostly fathers who worked outside of the home. So kids were practically jumping out of their seats to tell the music teacher what their parents did for a living. When he sang about the selected jobs all the kids were really enthusiastic and clapped with great energy when he was done.

I was sitting at the front of the classroom, and being a shy little kid, I didn't really want to be called on, so I just sat there with my shoulders hunched up trying to pull my head into my shell. As you might have guessed, my attempt at hiding was futile. He found me! "What does your daddy do?" I said I didn't know. He asked me if I knew what kind of business he worked for and I said he worked for my grandfather at the Hamburg Monument Company.

He asked me if my father cut letters. I said that I didn't know, but maybe. So the teacher started singing this little ditty about my father cutting letters. When he was finished only one or two kids clapped and I heard one little girl ask sarcastically, "What kind of job is that?"

As I advanced through the grades they got worse. Whenever a new friend would ask me what my dad did for a living and I told him or her, they would always go, "Ehww!"

When I was in the sixth grade, I got into a fight in the locker room after PE with this bully because he said for days on end that my dad screwed dead people. I was very naïve and knew nothing at all about sex, but I did know that my father was being insulted.

I was a really mild-mannered and shy kid who didn't anger easily and didn't like to fight so I tried to explain to him that my dad had never even seen dead people; he didn't work in a funeral home and the dead people were already in the ground by the time he got to them. But he insisted and persisted on calling my dad a necrophiliac, which made the other kids laugh.

He got right in my face and kept on with his tirade with his foul mouth and even fouler breath. I'd had enough! I pushed him as hard as I could against the wall. "Oh, ho, ho, you've had it now, Sanders," the entire class seemed to say.

His face was white hot! Just as I thought I was going to have to push him again or run, the PE teacher stepped in and stopped it. So this was when he demanded that I meet him at the park, which was where all of the neighborhood fights that meant anything took place.

He told me to meet him at four, which wasn't easy because I had to get home and change clothes and would have to dodge my mother who would insist on knowing where I was going.

The school was a mile away from home and I knew that I would have to run home instead of taking the bus. My house was the last stop on the route, and if I ran hard, I usually beat the bus by twenty minutes.

I got home quickly. Changed my clothes and jumped on my bicycle and flew back to the park. I could hear the horn that blew at four sharp that announced that first shift was over at the General Electric plant, but there was no Darrel.

One of my friends came riding up on his bicycle and asked me where Darrel was. I told him that I had no idea. He said that Darrel was a big chicken anyway. Oddly enough I wasn't afraid at all since Darrell wasn't there and that maybe I had dodged a fight.

A few other kids straggled up. They heard there was gonna be a fight. Several kids started deriding the absent warrior, but at quarter past the hour here came Darrel. He didn't look anxious to get there at all.

"What's the matter, Darrel? Did you forget what time it was?" asked one of the spectators.

"No! My mother made me do my chores, asshole!"

"Chores?" chortled several in unison.

"Leave him alone!" cried one of his supporters. "Let's get this fight going! He's gonna whoop your ass, Sanders!"

I was worried that he might. I had never been in a serious fight, and even though I wasn't Catholic, I think I said a couple of dozen "hell Marys," which of course still wasn't Catholic. I had so much adrenaline that if I had not been blocked by the growing circle of adolescents, I believe that I could have outrun a cheetah. But there was nowhere to go, and my thought was that, if I was going to die, then I would go out in a blaze of glory.

My mind wandered to the near future and I saw my family standing around and speaking of me with great pride in the past tense. "Yes, he might have lost his life, but the other kid knew that he was in a fight." My brothers were standing with great pride and my sisters were crying . . . Suddenly! One kid yelled as loud as he could that he was going to go get his sister's Barbie dolls!

We both snapped to and started off facing each other, moving inside the circle of slobbering spectators. I was watching and waiting for him to make a move. I was worried that he might have a tremendous anger stored up and a well-thought-out plan for my demise that would be hard to overcome.

"Come on! Throw the first punch, you motherfucker! You won't get me this time!"

I was incensed at his use of foul language so I moved in on him and faked a punch, which made him wince as he moved back. I really wanted him to throw the first punch so that I could try out the blocking moves that my brother, who was taking karate in college, had shown me a few weeks before.

We completed a couple of more circles and some knucklehead chimed in, "Y'all quit your dancing. We came here to see a fight, not a couple of little girls making love!"

So Darrel, who had been embarrassed earlier that day, took on a devilish appearance and fervently attacked with his crooked fangs exposed!

He was rearing back for a roundhouse punch, but before he could get half way into his swing, I popped him in the nose with a straight-on punch! He staggered backward a half step, and even more infuriated, he came at me again. This time he had his head slightly turned so that I couldn't get him in the nose, but instead I got him right below the eye with another straight-on punch. I was completely surprised by my own success.

It was ugly. I pummeled him silly, but to his credit, he wouldn't quit. This guy had never lost a fight and I had never been in one, but I had so much adrenaline built up that he never laid a hand on me. Finally, after we were both covered in blood, one of his friends pulled me away from him and one of my friends grabbed Darrel and took him out of the circle. Darrel was swearing up a storm and declared that if he had not been pulled away from me he was about to whip my ass! I still don't think so.

You might think it corny, but I was praying the whole fight and it really did seem like God was on my side. It could have been that all of that running, jumping, climbing, and never sitting still made me more of a beast than some jackass whose main source of exercise was running his mouth.

When I got home I tried to sneak into my bedroom without my mother seeing me, but before I could get the door closed, she came into my room and immediately saw my bloody clothes. As usual, I thought that I was in serious trouble so I figured to tell the truth.

"I got into a fight."

"It looks like it. It looks like he got the best of you! Who started the fight?"

"I guess I did."

"How many times have I told you to never start a fight? I've told you that if someone is picking on you, you have my permission to take care of it, but never throw the first punch!"

"Mom! I couldn't help it. I had to do something!"

"Why did you have to do something? Why didn't you go to the teacher if you had to do something? What did the other boy do?"

"He said something really bad about Dad."

I saw a slight change in her demeanor. She was losing a little of her "Gestapoesque" tone and reached out and stroked my head.

"Son, what was it he said?"

"He said that Dad screwed dead people. What does that mean, Mom? When he said, it, all the other kids laughed and I was so mad I couldn't help myself," I said while attempting to fight back tears.

Since I was still very very naïve, I thought Darrel meant that Dad ran screws into dead people.

"You'll know soon enough what he meant. It was very ugly what he said and I hope that you landed at least a couple of good punches. I don't understand, where did all that blood come from? You don't seem to have any cuts or scratches on you! Where did he hurt you?"

"Mom, he never even hit me. This is his blood! He was bleeding really bad and he kept trying to jump on me. There was one time we started rolling on the ground and his nose was bleeding all over me!"

Suddenly my mother smiled profusely and gave me a big hug and told me that she was very proud of me. Knowing that my mother was not angry proved that I really had won the day.

***

The next day when I went to school I did not know what to expect. Darrel had a lot of "friends" and I thought that they would exact revenge on me. I figured that Darrel would be waiting for me with a new strategy for taking me down and I was not mentally ready for an escalated battle.

Word very quickly had gone through the school that I had beaten the pulp out of Darrel. Much to my surprise, his friends were coming up to me before the bell rang, patting me on the back. There was a group of girls who were standing together talking quietly, and when they saw me, they started clapping and cheering.

Darrel had the respect of a bully only because he was feared. I had no idea that his mantle could be wrested from him so easily and at the same time I had no idea how to be a hero. The girls all wanted to come up to me and talk and tell me how proud they were but I quickly moved away from them, and fortunately for me, the bell rang to go inside.

Darrell and I actually became friends after that. It's really a shame that sometimes respect only comes from a firmly planted fist. But still, there is a lesson there.

I still caught hell from time to time from some people because of my father's occupation, but none of them would ever get too close to me. Unfortunately this stigma followed me for many years, but

I got used to it, especially after I started working at the monument company, and quite frankly, I liked being different from everyone else.

It caught me by surprise many years later when I told an attractive female what I did for a living and she said, "Oh cool! That sounds like a really neat job!"

Finally . . . There was my validation and of course I married her.

***

Sometimes a Sneeze
is Just a Sneeze

Besides being an early climber, I was also quiet handy with a hammer and saw. I built my first tree house at six years old, almost entirely by myself. I told my dad that I wanted one, so instead of building one for me, he told me of the time, at my exact age, that he helped his father replace the bearings in his Model T.

His words were actually very inspiring to me, and when he brought home a pile of discarded monument crates, I was very excited! I eagerly set about pulling out the nails and straightened them without being shown how. I then proceeded to cut, piece, and build. It wasn't very pretty, but by-god I did it!

When I got my first bicycle at seven years old, I took it completely apart, and unlike most kids, I put it back together with no parts left over. My dad watched the whole thing without flinching and commended me for a job well done.

In effect, when it came to mechanical or physical challenges, I had no trouble whatsoever, but when it came to people, especially girls, I had trouble. For a long time I had to settle for dreaming about girls.

Well, the truth is that dreams are better than the truth, unless you're a millionaire, and I bet they would say quit dreaming and get in there and do it.

You see, it's like this, where girls were concerned: when I was young, from like eleven to seventeen, whenever I had thoughts of pretty girls, I would sneeze. For some reason, I seemed to attract decent-looking girls who sometimes walked up to me to offer some chewing gum or whatever.

"Would you like a piece?" she would ask as she held out the gum.

Boom! I ejaculated a tremendous sneeze. I kid you not! It would start as a tingle between the thighs, but would somehow transform itself into an entirely different signal and would race its way through my body and would come forth from my engorged nose with a hardy blubber!

This was hardly the body fluid that any self-respecting girl would accept on her person, so I literally blew many chances at an early age of losing my virginity!

I learned quickly to avoid the close proximity of pretty girls and so was able to prevent the knowledge, of my infirmity, of becoming common.

Yes, plain-looking girls didn't do it to me, and that is why those were the ones I was able to hang out with. When I started dating they were the "lucky" ones to garner my attention, but I continued my celibacy because I was afraid that my volcanic proboscis would not allow the very natural course to take place, that is to say inter———, so I was always stuck with, for me, the very unnatural course, that is to say dis———.

That's right. I was no talker. I wanted serious conversation but it was difficult to find a willing accomplice. So all of my courses seemed to turn into the only one left, which was "obstacle."

I kept trying to evolve, but I was getting a reputation as either a nerd or a homosexual because I never even tried to do the "zipper-de-undo-dah" with the girls. My reputation was exposed to me by a female classmate who seemed to treat me with motherly annoyance. I was mortified and became determined to cast off my curse. I didn't know it at the time, but later I would long for the time when I was blessed with such a stalwart line of defense against the depredation of womanhood.

As soon as I could regroup I decided I would lose my virginity, which the thought of nearly landed me in the hospital due to an inexhaustible series of sneezes, which left me entirely dilapidated. Even though these eruptions blew forth, I chose steadfastly to slog ahead with my intentions to proactivate, but alas, I fear, even the Titans must have their Waterloo.

In the meantime, I kept seeing Holly in the hallways and noticed that, in spite of her exceptional good looks, I could look her in the eye, or anywhere else, without sneezing. I really thought that it was because I was not attracted to her due to the thrashing I received from her a few weeks earlier.

"I don't understand what's wrong with you," she came at me one day like a table leg in the dark. "Your reputation is in shambles!"

Oooo! Immediately I was a bit fizzy! I would expect almost any teenage girl to say "trashed" or "garbage" or "ruined" or simply "bad." But, Holly said "in shambles."

This seemed much more wistful to me, which is due to very low expectations of my fellow students who were obsessed entirely with what I couldn't be. You see, the other side of my reputation was that I was some kind of savant, which I wasn't. I think everyone always saw me with this discerning look, which made them think that I was always deep in thought, but the reality was that I was trying not to sneeze.

Not once during the seemingly interminable duration of being let in on this terrible secret by Holly, which was beforehand unbeknown only to me, did I have the urge. My exaltation grew exponentially as I realized that I was under complete control and that a perfect strategy for dealing with my impossible handicap was laid at my feet. I would now only see a girl's brains! Okay, so I slipped from time to time but I had met my Waterloo and I was Lord Wellington!

"What are you talking about?" I asked genuinely puzzled.

"Don't tell me that you don't know that you are being ridiculed by the entire school!"

"Why in the world are they talking about me? I'm nobody!"

"Recently everyone has noticed how you only hang out with ugly girls and dorks and how that whenever an attractive girl comes up to you, you can't wait to run away from her . . . People are beginning to think that you're queer."

Now . . . I know that "queer" is an ugly word, but I'm only trying to demonstrate what it was like years ago and to show you what
I had to endure.

"But I'm not a queer. I like pretty girls! It's just that every time
I get near one, I sneeze!"

"That is ridiculous!! You think anyone will buy that? Hey . . .
why aren't you sneezing now? Don't you think I'm pretty?"

"Wull, yeah but—"

"But what?"

"You're not . . . well, I'm not . . . well . . . thinking of . . . you
know—"

"NO! WHAT?"

"I'm not turned on."

"Well! Fuck you!" And those words nearly made me, but I
didn't. I didn't sneeze. It started, but then it stopped as though a tiny
martial artist was inside of me waiting for just such an opportunity to
karate kick that last sneeze right out of my arse end. Then she turned
and she left.

But she didn't leave my mind, and even now she's still in there,
that performer of miracles! And as I said after our encounter, I would
still see her in the halls and would look her in the eye with no effect
and I should add that apparently she felt no effect either . . . until one
day . . . there it was. The look . . . the connection.

Oddly enough, we had quit speaking to each other. We would
pass each other in the halls and just look. We didn't wave, we didn't
nod, nor did we wink. We just looked.

I wasn't sure what I was seeing in her face. It didn't look like
lust. (I knew what lust looked like because of all the horny bastards
in the school). All I knew was that every time I looked at her, it was
like being kicked in the stomach.

I never sneezed during this period because the sight of other
pretty girls no longer had a visceral effect on me. I didn't look at her
slender waist or her round behind, and to tell you the truth, I don't
recall looking at her boobs. My best friend and confidante did not
believe a word of it. I don't think I realized it until years later, but
Holly really was the prettiest girl in the school.

One day out of the blue Holly approached me and asked me to go to a movie. I told her that I would have to think about it so she turned around and walked off. *What an idiot!* I thought to myself and watched her turn the corner out of sight.

I took off running and expected to catch her but instead ran right into the assistant principal. I got five demerits, but it turned out okay because Holly heard about it, thought it was cute, and we started dating.

The junior-senior dance was right around the corner and of course she expected me to go. Like many boys I was a crappy dancer and didn't want to go, but told her I would anyway. Springtime allergies are hell!

She called my house on the day of the dance, and when I went to the phone, I started sneezing. I tried with all my might to hold it back, but I was not very successful. She decided to come over to my house, presumably to see if she could help.

When she arrived my brother answered the door. She asked my brother if I was still sneezing. He told her that he didn't know what she was talking about, that he had not heard me sneeze all day. She asked him if he was sure about that to which he replied that he had been there all day and had not heard me sneeze one time except for when I was on the telephone.

Well damn! By listening to my brother's testimony she believed that I had been faking when I was on the phone with her. The absolute truth was that my brother had been over at the lake most of the day and had not come home until about the time that I was on the phone with Holly. When I entered the living room, she was standing with her arms folded and giving me the death stare.

"So you have hayfever do you?"

"Yes, I have hayfever. I took an allergy pill while ago . . . Maybe it'll start working . . . ," I said, then sneezed.

"Oh, come on! I know you're faking!"

"No! Honestly I'm not! I really want to go to the dance!" I lied.

She stood there tapping her toes and pursing her lips, and I'm sure, cursing me in her mind. Good grief! Couldn't she see my reddened eyes and catarrh-inflicted nose? It *was* northwest Georgia, for crying out loud!

"All right," she said. "Come pick me up at six o'clock. You better be dressed and you better have my orchid. My mother is going to take our picture and you better have your sneezing out of your system!"

Well shit! I was going to the dance. I went to pick her up and her mother was there with camera in hand and took our picture as I pinned the orchid on Holly's dress.

The dance was in the school gymnasium, and when we entered, one of Holly's best friends came over and leaned over to hug her, which gave me a really good view of her boobs and I'll be damned if I didn't sneeze like a son of a gun! I wasn't sure if the allergy pill had worn off or if it really was the boobs. Could have been either.

To Holly, *one* and *two*, it was the boobs! I could not convince her otherwise and that was the beginning of the end. We barely spoke on the way home, and when I dropped her off, she didn't even look at me as she got out of the car and went inside. At first I was really numb, and then as I got close to my house, I started laughing and didn't stop until I got inside. (I always laughed at bullshit problems! I wonder, if St. Peter tells me that I'm banned from entering the pearly gates will I laugh?)

I tried calling her on the phone, but our conversations were always really short. She kept telling me to try her a couple of days later, but after the third attempt at getting a date with her, I hung up the phone and said, "To hell with this!"

Strangely enough, about three months later, her mother called me and wanted to know why I quit calling Holly. I told her that I thought she didn't want to see me anymore to which she replied that Holly had been moping around for two and a half months waiting for me to call. I told her that I was sorry, but I had moved on.

When I went to work at the monument company full-time and was working around all that dust, I would sometimes sneeze. My father never could understand why I would bust out laughing and I never told him. Eventually my tendency to laugh subsided, but everybody who was around me on a regular basis never quit thinking that I was a nut!

***

Just a Thought

I grew up near the end of the hippie movement and believed their rant on the evils of capitalism. I knew that I wouldn't have to worry about where to put my money because I'd never have any. Later on, when computers became commonplace, I figured I wouldn't have to learn to use one. What good would one do in a cemetery? Yes, in effect, I could stay in the Stone Age. Okay, sorry for that ill attempt at humor.

Once a friend asked if I had a passport to which I replied, "I didn't think I needed one to go to Alabama!"

So you might say that I was a stick in the mud—averse to change. I was completely comfortable with mediocrity!

But! As the back doesn't bend as well nor do the knees and the hands don't grip and the eyes don't see so well, it becomes apparent that computers have their place and making a lot of money has its advantages and mediocrity sometimes fails to pay the piper. I knew that I was going to have to figure something out. Did I mention Bobby and our harebrained adventure?

***

Arnold and Anthony

The openness of our shop attracted the attention of children who lived nearby. We made friends with many young boys who were morbidly curious to see what was going on inside. Were there bodies in there too? No, we'd say. They always seemed slightly let down by this revelation.

One especially curious lad was a nine-year-old, slow-witted black child named Arnold. There is relevance to the mention of his color, which later I hope you will understand. My dad was very kind to Arnold who took to him quite readily. I too befriended him and began asking him about his life. Our attitude toward him encouraged him to become a regular visitor.

He was born to a very sick alcoholic mother whose hips were so narrow that it seemed they had caused Arnold's head to squeeze into a very narrow shape. It caused his eyes to sit more to the side of his face than the front and caused his mouth to protrude a little like a fish. When we first met, he had no idea who his father was, but he did know his brother who lived with him and his mother in the housing projects, which were around the corner from our business. Later on, out of no-where, the father showed up and he too reluctantly got to know him.

His brother's name was Anthony who looked mostly normal except that his head was slightly too small for his body. In fact, at six years old, his head looked to have adult-like proportions to his body, making him look more like a dwarf than a child. He excelled at his impression of an iceberg. One wondered if he would ever get where he was going.

Arnold talked in a slow monotone, which was slower even than the typical Southerner. Even though we were fairly busy, we would

131

make allowances for his near-daily visit to our little compound because we enjoyed his inquisitive, though dull, nature.

His brother would follow him, but on most days he just stood staring at us from the other side of the street. If Arnold stayed too long, Anthony would simply turn around without saying a word and go home.

I imagined Anthony having an angel guiding him around and protecting him, because he was always alone unless he was with Arnold. No matter the circumstances he never came to any harm. I always had this deep sense of sorrow for him, knowing that he was oblivious to the idea that the world was ready to consume him, but because of his absolute innocence he was immune to its predations. I prayed that was the case anyway.

On the other hand, Arnold's angel needed a little help, because he was always into mischief. In fact, the first time that we ever saw him, with his ass straight in the air, he was pushing a single roller-skate down the middle of the street with traffic zooming past at forty to fifty miles per hour on either side, some swaying onto the shoulder, others seemingly as oblivious to him as he was to them.

He never looked up, he never waved, and he never flinched whenever someone laid down on their horn! My dad and I watched him until he disappeared, and then we turned toward each other with that little one-sided grin that says you're not sure you saw what you thought you saw.

"He's gonna get killed as sure as a dog always shits in somebody else's yard," Dad said. He said things like that. It brings your blood pressure down a bit when you look at things with a little humor. We felt like we had witnessed a miracle of divine intervention, and Dad was relieved that we hadn't witnessed a little kid turned into a pinwheel!

Whenever we would see this again, my father and I would yell at him to get out of the street. Since we didn't believe it the first time that we saw it, it took more than once for us to respond. We gave up trying to sway him from his activity because he totally ignored us, so we assumed he was either deaf or retarded, and we were afraid that if we intervened physically that we could cause a worse disaster.

We tried calling the police, but I believe that they thought we were pulling their leg.

It was after a hiatus of several days that he showed up at our place with a plaster cast on his right arm. He simply walked in without a word and stood looking at us. As I said we didn't know whether he was deaf or not but my father spoke to him anyway.

"I see you have a cast on your arm," said my father.

"Yayuh."

"Did you break it?"

"Yayuh."

"How did you break it?"

He giggled a kind of slow breathy giggle. "I got run over by a caaarrr."

"Was it because you were pushing that skate down the middle of the street?"

"Naw, I was driving my caaarrr down the street."

He held the skate out with his good hand. "Would you like to hab it 'cause I can't drive it wid one hand?"

"No, thank you, son. You'll need it later when that arm heals."

"Were you driving it down the middle of the street when you got run over?" I asked.

"Naw, they said I couldn't drive it down the middle of the street no more so I moved over like everbody else."

"Who told you you couldn't drive down the middle of the street?"

"The po-lice."

"You mean they didn't make you get out of the street?"

"Naw, they jus' said I couldn't be goin' down the middle of the street like I was."

"How in the world did you keep from getting killed?" I asked.

"'Cause Jesus was watching out for me."

A melancholy came over me as he spoke that comes with the resignation of reality. He told us of his mother and how she was going to Hell because she didn't believe in God. He told us of how he and Anthony walked to church every Sunday regardless of the weather. It didn't matter that neither one of them could read their

Bible; they carried it with them anyway. I noticed later on that no matter what day it was, Anthony always was carrying a small book, which was indeed his Bible.

All the other neighborhood children hung together, but Arnold and Anthony only hung with each other. I asked them if they had any friends but they said no. When I asked them why they didn't, they only shrugged.

Later, when a group of their peers stopped in to check us out, we struck up a conversation. I asked them if they knew Arnold and his brother.

"Yeah, he's crazy!" exclaimed the one named Carl.

"Why do you say that?" I asked in earnest.

The others, I think there were five or six, all looked at each other and almost in unison rolled their eyes and gave a bit of a shudder.

"Whatchu mean? Hain'tchu ever seen him pushin' that skate down the middle of the road?" sang Carl.

"Is that all?"

Another little boy grabbed his own face and pulled back his cheeks to emulate Arnold's face. The surprising thing was that the other boys didn't laugh. It looked to me that they may have been a little afraid of him instead.

"You know he can't help the way he looks?"

They shook their heads as if they didn't know it.

"Do any of ya'll ever play with Arnold?"

They collectively denied ever having played with Arnold or Anthony and they looked like they were ready to run.

"His mother is a witch!" cried the one called Odell.

"How do you know that?" I asked.

"'Cause she cries out at night and curses God an' an' beats Anthony 'cause he don't never say nothin' an' she tells Arnold he was born of the devil and it's his fault he looks like he does," said the one called Grady.

"My mother says she wears devil charms," said Carl.

A pall came over our little group so I tried to make light of the situation. I told them that they should be kind to Arnold and his brother, and try to understand that it was not their fault that they were different. I said a lot of other things to try to inspire them, including that Martin Luther King would be proud to see them accepting those boys into their foal. Maybe that was a cheap trick, using Martin Luther King, but I felt like someone had to start somewhere!

I figured that I wasted my breath, but a few days later, I saw one of the boys pulling Arnold in a Western flyer wagon with his bicycle. Arnold was beaming! I was truly touched, but then I thought, what if they were doing this so they can hurt him?

My instincts were wrong, sort of. He did get hurt, but it wasn't on purpose, and I was glad, not that he was hurt, but that it wasn't on purpose. I saw them walking around with scraped knees and Arnold with a scraped forehead and a chipped tooth, but he was happy. He had friends, and one had actually given him a Coke.

One other day I saw another boy trying to teach Arnold how to ride a bicycle, yet to no avail. It inspired Arnold to get one, but the one he found was missing the front wheel so he was reduced to holding it up and pushing it, which he did all over town.

Arnold never learned how to ride a bicycle, but he always had one. One day I saw him with a bike with two wheels, the next day . . . front wheel removed.

I had to concede his reasoning behind removing the front wheel. He said that if it had both wheels he might try to ride it and then he would get hurt, no ifs, ands, or buts! If he removed the rear wheel the bike just flopped around and he could get tangled up in it.

Another day he was pushing the bike, with both wheels attached, toward the grocery store. When he returned he had a huge box balanced on the bar with two bags of groceries in it. A lady had given him a dollar to go to the store for her, along with enough money to buy the groceries.

As difficult as it is to believe no one ever bothered Arnold during that time and eventually other people began paying him to run all sorts of errands for them, and sure enough you would see him all over town, pushing that bicycle with goods on board.

Arnold was inspired! Eventually he made enough money to buy a garden cart and then a lawn mower. He had saved almost all the money that he earned in a pickle can that he had hidden on our property underneath an old discarded tombstone, that a generation before me, had been thrown down a twenty-foot-deep embankment.

I had seen him down there and fussed at him to get out from there lest he get hurt. He always said yes sir, that he wouldn't go down there anymore, but he did anyway. I got more than annoyed with him, but I figured that his dull wit made him forget.

He was a damn sight smarter than anyone thought he was, including me, because he hid that money in a place that no-one would have ever looked. His friends still thought he was crazy for playing in such a seemingly dangerous place so they never followed him down there. Of course the snake he pulled out of its hidey-hole by the tail, then turned to share the thrill with his friends, was a major deterrent.

Even though his mother knew he was getting money for errands, she thought he was getting nickels and dimes for them—to her that was all he was worth.

Anthony tried his hand at making money the same way but he didn't seem to have the knack for it, but one day he came into the shop with a miniature rocking chair made from a single beer can that was amazingly detailed.

I tried to give him four dollars for the tiny chair to which he said nothing, but gave a gradual smile and turned slowly toward his home without the money. Gradually I wound up with a set of four chairs and miniature porch swing that I finally convinced him that it was all right to take the money.

He started bringing in other beer can sculptures that became more and more intricate. One that he brought was an old-style covered wagon that was made from several cans that must have taken him many hours to complete. I didn't really have enough money to pay him but he gave it to me anyway.

It seemed to me that Anthony was autistic. If people didn't have the money in their hand right then and there, he would just give them the sculpture. When they tried to give him a few dollars later, he would turn away from them and go home without a word or a gesture.

Anthony wound up in Dog Trot, Alabama, living with his half sister from his father's first marriage. Dog Trot was a popular arts and crafts center in the northeastern mountains of Alabama, which gave Anthony an outlet for his art.

As I said, I still saw him around, so one day I asked him what he was up to. By this time Anthony was in his mid-twenties and had learned to drive, but he continued to walk everywhere when he was in town. But the most striking difference was in his confidence when he spoke and the light that radiated from him when he recognized me.

He told me where he was living and that I should come to see him. He also said that he brought his mother money to live on every month and that he had moved her from the projects and bought her a car.

It was hard to believe his manner and sophistication, due to his history, but it piqued my curiosity so I went to Dog Trot. There you will find a crossroad, and about a half-dozen old buildings that were once used for something else but are now being used for arts and crafts, you know . . . pioneer . . . rustic . . . junk.

Anthony had leased his own building, which was full of everything you can imagine. He was still making metal can sculptures but had graduated to other things. He learned to paint, very primitive religious paintings. He learned to restore old phonographs—I found an old Spike Jones 78 for a dollar but I couldn't afford the player . . . and old treadle sewing machines and claw foot bath tubs with the correct brass fittings and you name it.

I went into another store, figuring that I could get the straight dope on Anthony and was shocked to learn how much money he had made.

"So you know Anthony?"

"Oh yeah. Since he was like six years old."

"So did you know him when he first started sculptin'?"

"Well sure, I still have the very first thing he ever did."

I saw a twinge of excitement that was quickly extinguished by the old lady as she was trying not to betray her interest in my previously unknown treasure.

"So what is this particular piece? Pray tell!"

That was the first time I had actually ever heard anyone say "pray tell" and was more fascinated by this than I was by her ancient mole between her nose and her lip, or the fact that she was curious about my little rocking chair.

"So when did you acquire said piece?"

So how many people do you know that begin every sentence with "so" and say "pray tell" and "acquire said piece"? Was I talking to the prosecution? Or was she just eccentric? I vote eccentric.

"Well, let's see . . . I had known him for about three or four years so I would say around seventy-nine or eighty . . . Why?" I was worried I might get it wrong!

"So what is this said piece?"

"It's just a little rocking chair made out of a beer can."

"Hmmm . . . ," she said nodding her head. "So is there anything scratched underneath the seat?"

"I don't know. I don't think I ever looked. Why? What would he have scratched underneath the seat?"

"If I tell you, you might try to forge his mark if it's not an original."

"What? Did he try to pass some off as originals that weren't his?" Are you kidding me! She was acting like these little sculptures were priceless or something.

"Well, we know that he said that he marked all of his own, but his father came here once and told people that he had shown Anthony how to make those sculptures and made it sound like he let Anthony have some of his, early on, to sell. Anthony didn't like it that his father was taking credit for every single piece so he started making his mark on them."

The fact is that the first piece Anthony gave me was not marked, but more than likely it was his. When I saw the father not long after I had first met Anthony, he was a very shaky individual who would have had trouble making anything. Of course he shook violently enough at times that it might have actually aided in his making babies. Well . . . who knows?

I went home and took the chair off its shelf and looked at the bottom and found no mark. Even so, it only made sense that Anthony's first pieces wouldn't have the mark since it was only after he was succeeding that his father made the claim.

A week or two later, I returned to Dog Trot and showed Anthony that I still possessed his little rocker. He was visibly touched and reached out so I placed it in his hand where he stared for the longest time. I have no idea what he was thinking as he said nothing; he just handed it back.

"Isn't this your first piece?" I asked.

"Yes . . . I made this chair on September 27, 1981. I finished it at 11:26 PM. My mother was asleep and so was Arnold. My pops was at his girlfriend's house so there warn't no one to make me go to sleep."

I wondered if it bothered him to know that his father had a girlfriend. It did not seem to.

"Anthony, the lady next door says your stuff is worth a lot of money. Do you want to go next door with me to see what she'll give for it?"

"Sure."

So, pray tell, what do you think she offered? I'll give you a hint. Her pupils dilated very quickly but she kept her poker face.

"So, I see it has no mark," she said.

"Anthony says he'll swear on a stack of bibles that it is his first piece."

"Yes'm. I made it on September 27th, 1981. I finished it at 11:26 PM."

"I'll give you fifty dollars," she said.

"I guess that means it's worth at least a hundred," I said.

"I'll give you four hundred," said Anthony as he pulled out the money.

"Anthony, that's crazy!" I exclaimed. "I should give it back to you."

"Why? It's yours. I gave it to you."

"All right!" she cried. "I'll give you one fifty."

"I don't want you to have it," said Anthony.

"It's not for sale," I said.

We went back to Anthony's shop and had a laugh and a root beer. Well, as much as he had ever laughed. His was barely audible.

We parted company with a gentle handshake and I went back home with an uneasy feeling. It was not long before the flimsy beer can was introduced and Anthony's bread and butter dried up. It might not have mattered much anyway because an ominous power was about to descend upon the independent young black man.

An official-looking man with a briefcase entered the store one day and presented Anthony with a card that said "Harold Hardacher – field agent – Internal Revenue Service."

Anthony had never paid any taxes—ever! He didn't know about rules. He only knew the rules of survival. There was a man who wanted Anthony's niche in Dog Trot. It was he who turned him in.

Alabama revenue agents found out, both internal and sales and use division. It was over for Anthony. They all told him that he had x number of hours to produce some paperwork and that he best get a lawyer.

Anthony was overwhelmed, as you would be too, but his autistic mind had no faculty for such catastrophies. So he left. All of the agents were watching for him to leave by car, but he went out a cellar door and down through a kudzu patch to the highway back to Georgia where he walked the entire fifty-six miles back to his father's apartment in the projects without stopping. Twenty hours straight!

When his father opened the door after hearing a faint knock, he found his son standing there with the look of death. Though Mr. Gaines was not a particularly good man, he was not an evil one, so with some compassion, he led Anthony into the living room and got him to sit down.

Very slowly Anthony asked for a glass of water to which his father eagerly complied.

"Son, what in the world brings you here at this hour?"

"The law."

"The law?"

"They was going to put me in jail."

Mr. Gaines went to the door and peeked out to see if anyone was outside.

"Son, where's yo car? Did they follow you?" Mr. Gaines asked excitedly.

"No, sir. I don't reckon they followed me. My car's still in Alabama."

"Whatchu mean it's in Alabama? You tellin' me you walked all the way from yo store?"

"Yes, sir . . . I brung you this. Give some to mama," he said as he handed him a wad of cash that amounted to around fourteen thousand dollars.

Mr. Gaines's eyes got huge as he took the money.

"Pop, you reckon I can stay here a while?"

"Yes, son. You is more than welcome!"

With that Anthony went to sleep.

The IRS never found him. He had never gotten a social security number nor a driver's license and his car was bought with cash and was put in the lady's name who owned the building where he worked.

A social worker did find him, but it was her job to enroll him in the federal welfare program, which is when he got his first social security card.

Almost the exact same fate befell his brother Arnold. His yard business was doing very well. He had graduated from the small garden cart and push mower to an Oldsmobile 88 with a trailer hitch and a trailer. He proudly drove all over the northeast of town towing his trailer and a "slightly used" zero turn mower. His equipment also included two weed trimmers and a couple of push mowers and of course some rakes and a broom.

He had gotten enough business to bring in around eight hundred dollars per week when the weather was good and around three hundred dollars a week when it turned too cold for grass cutting. This activity roused the greed in one of his "friends" who convinced him that he needed a manager. This manager "friend" ticked off my father who told Arnold that he was being taken advantage of and that he should fire him.

Arnold said that he would, but the next time that he came around to cut our grass, the manager was still with him. Dad told him, "No! Fire the manager and you can come back."

This hurt Arnold's feelings, but the next time he came around his manager was gone. Arnold revealed that other clients had advised him to do the same. The manager, it turns out, was also using Arnold to gain access to people's houses so that he could rob them.

Having been fired, the manager turned Arnold in. The difference between Arnold and Anthony was that Arnold had gotten a social security number and driver's license and had a valid address. The manager had also kept a ledger of Arnold's receipts for about two months. The IRS, as they have a right to do, clamped down on him and estimated that Arnold owed them around eight thousand dollars.

Arnold sold everything he had, which amounted to less than two thousand dollars, and gave them about two thousand more dollars that he had saved, to keep from going to jail. Of course the IRS settled with him, which relieved poor Arnold's mind. Just as bad though, he was also receiving welfare at the same time that he was making money so the Welfare Department came after him too.

Fortunately, due to Arnold's status, they let it go and he was allowed with much fanfare and celebration to return to the projects where he languished for many years until he died of kidney failure.

After Arnold's funeral, I did not see Anthony for several years because he had gone back to Alabama to live with his sister. But one day, as I was working in the cemetery across from the shop, I felt this strong pull to turn around. There was a lonely-looking fellow just standing there staring. I turned back to work, and after several times of doing this, I realized that it was Anthony. I also realized that he was waiting for me to wave, so I did. He returned my wave and then . . . he was gone.

***

A New Friend

It was wet. I was on my daily walk on the college grounds and was having to dodge the incessant puddles. I was looking down, hopping from side to side on the muddy road and did not see the runner who was doing the same, who did not see me, so in as such we collided. *Plomp, thwuck* . . . I had fallen . . . mud all over. The clothes didn't matter, but the glasses did; they were covered in muddy water, impairing my already faulty vision.

The runner fared no better. Exasperated, he looked at me with contempt I thought, but then again I couldn't really see his expression. What I imagined that I was seeing belied the fact that I was hearing sudden laughter.

I thought for a second that it was Bobby, since the runner's laughter seemed so familiar, yet it was a more tamped down version, like he was just trying to get the banshee into a better mood. When I cleaned my glasses, I was astounded at how much he indeed did look like Bobby!

Beside the runner stood a panting rotund little blue heeler that had enough sense not to join the fracas. The intelligence in the dog's eyes matched its owner's.

"Man, I'm sorry. I didn't see you or hear you coming!" I exclaimed.

"Are you all right?" he half chuckled.

"Yeah, I'm fine. Lucky it was muddy or we might have gotten hurt," I replied as I stood up wiping my muddy mouth with an only slightly less muddy sleeve.

"Yep, of course if it hadn't been muddy we wouldn't have run into each other . . . ergo . . ." He chuckled again.

I could see that he liked to laugh. (Could be the pollen that sometimes measures in the thousands, which also explains why there is so much snot blowing out of peoples noses!)

"Well, have a nice run," I said.

"Yeah, enjoy the rest of your walk . . . try to stay out of the mud!"

With that he and the dog, that I heard him call Dingus, puttered on down the road. I watched him, for a minute or so, no longer dodging the puddles but enthusiastically splashing on through. The dog, however, missed every one, wagging its tail every time the runner madly introduced himself to one. In another instant he was gone. I wondered if I should have at least introduced myself to him.

No matter; it occurred to me that he too could have introduced himself to me so I shrugged and continued on to my car. It also occurred to me that he, like me, could possibly be an introvert. Two introverts, by nature, rarely become friends. Who will make the first move?

I continued my three times weekly walks wondering who else I might run into. Nothing of significance happened until one day, way up on the mountain, I encountered a veritable buzz saw. It was a ghastly machine that had great huge tires and a hinge in the middle that allowed its torso to bend around obstacles to get to its prey. It was a steroid laden metal dung beetle with a double set of pincers and a circulating saw for a tongue. When its ligneous victims were caught in its hungry jaws, the tongue would jut rapidly out and take a lick straight through them one at a time, and being dissatisfied with its taste, it would lay it down and move rapidly on to its next meal until an entire hillside was littered with corpses.

No corpse laid very long for another beast would hook them and drag them rapidly to another machine to strip them naked of all their limbs and pile them so they could be taken away to serve the fancy of mankind.

I was depressed at the loss of so many of my truest of friends. I had known these trees since I was six years old when I had ridden bicycles with my brother and two of his friends to this very spot. I was now twenty-eight and was just as inspired by them up until this moment as then. There were piles of logs that were awaiting their final destiny, weeping from every wound.

My walk was cut short. My legs were heavy. My soul was heavier. I do not remember the return walk to my car. I do not remember the drive home. I do remember pulling into my driveway and wondering whether or not I had breathed the whole way home.

That evening I ate very little, and when I went to bed, I slept very little. My wife of that time was sympathetic to my condition, but refused to join me in my melancholy. I was angry at society and felt guilty for being part of it. I vowed to change what I could.

The next morning I got up thinking that "today will truly be the first day of my newly found purposeful life. I will make a difference." I went about my morning business with the welling up of a prideful resolve.

When I was finished relieving one of the more important wellings of my morning's business, I reached for the roll of the necessary sanitary device. I hesitated, incapacitated with confusion. I felt hopelessly lost at the notion that what I had seen the day before was nothing compared to the indignity of what I was about to bestow upon the humble remains of one of its fallen brothers.

My spirits sank as I watched my resolve flowing round and round, down and away . . . reality stinks . . .

I moped around a week or two more, still suffering the pangs of defeat—the defeat of a morality that could be taken apart by toilet paper. What cause could be so uniquely destroyed? Which is worse, toilet paper or the "want" of toilet paper? Would I condemn the asses of billions of people to the torture of corn husks or clamshells just to save a few trees?

My spirit began to rebound when I thought that if merely half of the western world would sacrifice this decadence, then so would I. But wouldn't the necessity of more corn disrupt the balance of production? Wouldn't the need for more clamshells destroy more otherwise undisturbed clams? Damn it! I wished that I could find the receipt on this damn guilty conscience that my mother had given me so that I could take it back to the store and swap it for an ice cream cone or something that wouldn't last so damn long!

I decided to give the woods and my psyche time to heal so I concentrated on work. We had enough work to keep me busy during normal hours, but not enough to stay over. Being the restless type, when I'm not productively occupied, after three or four weeks I decided to begin work on refreshing my 1969 British Racing Green MGB GT. It was my daily driver, so basically, I was going to do a minor overhaul on all of the components that wouldn't take too long.

There was a car parts place close to our shop, so one rainy afternoon, I went there to purchase some of the items that were available to me. This particular store was never very busy so I went straight to the counter where no one was manning it. I heard a voice from the back that sounded vaguely familiar, asking me to please give it a minute, but I could not place it.

As I stood there waiting, out from behind the counter casually strolled a Blue Heeler. It made its way to my leg and gently sniffed and wagged its tail. Looking up at me his expression said, "I know you. You're the one that knocked over my nanny."

"I know you too," I said.

With that Dingus went back around the counter and stood half way into the back room wagging his tail slowly until the voice came out to take his station behind the counter. The voice and the runner were one in the same, and so was the laugh, which came forth easily when he recognized me.

"How are you, what can I do for you?" he asked. "Do you need any tar . . . or maybe MUUD remover?" he quipped.

"Very funny. No. I'm telling you, I had to quit going out there."

"Why? Because of all of the clear cutting they're doing?"

"Exactly! Man! It's really pissing me off!"

"Yeah, me too."

"Are you still going out there to run?"

"Not as much. Everywhere I go they're cutting or getting ready to cut."

"Man!" I just shook my head and looked at the floor . . . We talked about the college and half the world's woes for another half hour until I realized the time and, still without introducing myself, told him that I needed to return to work.

"Was there something you needed?" he asked.

"Oh crap! Yes, there is. I forget things when I get like this," I said half embarrassed, and proceeded to give my order which he quickly retrieved without once looking in the computer . . . they didn't use computers back then and a good parts man would generally know many hundreds, if not thousands of parts without looking them up.

He thanked me for my purchase, and as I was leaving, he asked me where I worked. I told him "Hamburg Monument Co."

"Oh really? That's where my mother bought my father's tombstone."

"Really? What was your father's name?"

"Dr. Barry Milton McStotts, same as mine except without the Dr. and with a Jr. My mother has known your father since he was a boy. Her father was the founder of Highfield Funeral Home."

"Then your grandfather knew my grandfather! In fact they were good friends . . . Your grandfather died in the fifties, didn't he?" I said as I wondered why he gave me his full name. I knew later, when I found out what an eccentric fellow he truly was.

"No, it was the sixties."

"Oh, okay, . . . well, I better get back to work. It was nice meeting you, Barry, or is it Milton?"

"No, it's Barry . . . same here. Thanks for coming in."

As I was driving down the road, I realized that I still hadn't told him my name. What *would* my mother think?

***

This Is Bullshit

"This is bullshit!" he blurted, he being Barry.

"What is?" I asked.

"This!"

"What?"

"This! All of this! It's all bullshit!" he decried as he waved his right arm at all the world around us.

"What in the world are you talking about?"

"All of this! These houses, the cars, the power lines! People . . . their false lives filled with banality . . . They're fucked up, all of them!" he railed again while swinging his arm violently, shaking the truck in the process.

This was the spring of 1992, and close to the one year anniversary of Barry's employment with us. The parts store over the hill from us had been sold three years earlier, which was six years after I had met him. He had continued to work for the parent store for two more years, but since he was the last one hired, he was the first one fired. This was during the period when corporate auto parts stores were pushing out the individually owned stores.

After his dismissal, he was out of work for two or three months and was getting depressed. We needed some help so I told my brother about Barry. He agreed that we should give him a try, so we hired him.

For the first year he was the hardest working, happiest-go-lucky s.o.b I had ever seen. We worked our tails off during this time and thought that we had the greatest employee of all time, which is why his tirade shocked me.

There was absolutely no warning, as we loaded the truck, that he was about to go off. We got our gas and snacks . . . nothing. We rode toward the next cemetery . . . nothing. We cleared the city limits and reached the country . . . boom!

Not being a psychiatrist I couldn't diagnose him as a schizophrenic, but based on the evidence they both definitely got my vote.

On and on he went. His eyes were white hot; his face was filled with anger . . . hatred even. I allowed him to vent for the forty minutes it took to get to the cemetery, but when we arrived, I told him to get a grip on himself.

"I said get a grip, not a gripe! We have got work to do!"

He got the shovels. He got the string. He got the wooden blocks and the hammer and the wheelbarrow, the hand trucks; he unloaded everything including what we didn't need except for the monument, which was the only thing that was proper since it needed to come off last any way.

He dug the hole for the foundation in three minutes and took my shovel away from me while I was trying to mix the concrete in the wheelbarrow and mixed it himself and poured it into the hole.

As I leveled the concrete, he hooked up the base and had it off the truck before I could finish. I gave him the evil eye, which finally connected with him and he slowed.

"What in the hell is the matter with you!?" I cursed, which was really hard for me to do. I rarely cursed back then, but when I did, people listened.

"I'm sick of it! Sick of the world . . . *everything* sucks!"

"Yeah, well, so what? I'm sick of it too, but who isn't?"

"Stupid people! They're too stupid to know how bad it is."

"Sometimes things are only as bad as you make them. Don't make things worse by pitching a fit!"

"They *are* worse than you think!"

"Is something wrong at home?"

"No."

"Is something wrong with your dog?"

"No."

"Are you sick? Do you have cancer?"

"No."

"Is it a girl?"

"No!"

"Then what's wrong? Why are you so miserable?"

"Everything! Everything is wrong! The whole bullshit fucked up world is wrong!"

Does this make sense to you? It didn't to me either. (Not the world being fucked up, that's a given, but his tirade is another matter.)

"I tell you what then," I said, "shut up and let's get to work and finish this stone, or I'll contribute a whole bunch more to your ill will toward this goddam world!"

Finally! He shut up. Barry worked the rest of the day with the idea that any more talking might be a little too expensive. When it was time to close up and go home, he left with a hang-dog look and simply said, "See ya . . . tomorrow."

It seemed to me that Barry was one of those manic depressives. When he was in his manic state, I would tell him that he was one of those "maniac depressives," which made him laugh. Of course when people are in their manic state, they just about always laugh. Barry would laugh at the oddest times including laughing at some of my terrible jokes and he would laugh at being told what to do.

When he was in his depressive state, it seemed that he could hardly move. After staying quiet for a couple of days, he would start his rant again. This pattern went on for about a year until the rest of us got to the point that we would give him a "government paid vacation," which is to say that we temporarily laid him off, claiming lack of work as the reason. (It wasn't an outright lie because he lacked in his work). He seemed to like this arrangement okay.

Of course his mother wasn't very happy with it. You see, it was because Barry was still living with her in her attic that she had fixed up for him. He actually had lived on his own a couple of times and was married for two weeks, but got divorced after he dumped water on his new wife because she wouldn't get up at 6:00 AM to go hiking with him.

One time when he was on one of his rants and complaining about the excess population, my brother suggested that he could reduce that number by "one" very easily.

"How am I supposed to do that?" Barry asked.

"You shoot yourself. I'll loan you the gun. I've got one in my car. Of course I guess if you shoot yourself and I don't know where you do it, I might as well give you the gun."

Of course my brother said this without knowing that Barry had already tried to kill himself twice by drug overdose. Both times Barry awoke in the hospital staring at his very ticked off mother.

"That's ridiculous! I hate guns . . . I don't want to be anywhere near one."

The truth is he was so delusional that he figured that if drugs didn't kill him that a gun probably wouldn't either. The bullet would probably just bounce off of his thick skull.

"That's what I figured . . . You want someone else to get rid of themselves. You want someone else to take responsibility. You don't want to do the dirty work."

"No, I want people to quit having babies. I've done my part there and I'd like for a natural disaster to take out a bunch of people."

"So you want a natural disaster that might take out your own mother. Is that what you want? I mean, how are you gonna pick and choose who a natural disaster gets rid of?"

"It doesn't really matter who it gets, but I know that I'll be in a safe place."

"Bullshit!"

My dad heard most of the conversation and intervened with the command that not getting any work done was also bullshit. So they got back to work.

After somewhere around four or five two-week government paid vacations, Barry's mother insisted that he look for another job. He lucked into one of the most perfect jobs that one of his stature could ever have. He went to work as a groundskeeper at Mountain College.

I had to admit that I was going to miss his manic phase, but his depressive phase was another story. Of course, he laughed at this statement and told me not to worry, that we would stay friends forever. Forever is a long time. But we did stay friends for a very long time.

***

After about a year as a groundskeeper Barry caught his break. On top of the highest peak at the college, there was a resort area that was composed of a very large rustic log cabin, a relatively tall stone fire tower, a modest caretaker's cabin, a well-stocked shop building and of course it was sitting on four beautiful garden laden acres. This is where Barry had always wanted to work since he was a child.

The resort had been taken care of by a very amicable fellow named Luther Hornsby who liked watching lightning storms from the fire tower. One particular day, there had been lightning storms firing off all day and Mr. Hornsby was beside himself with glee.

He had been in the fire tower nearly all day and his wife decided that he had had enough. She came out of the little cabin and vigorously motioned for her husband to come down and come inside. The husband, however, had other ideas and he motioned for her to go away.

It would probably have been a good idea if he had listened to his wife. Just as she turned to go back inside, a tremendous bolt of lightning struck the tower and blew a small stone out of the wall that struck him on the back of the head . . . But that didn't kill him. It did, however, knock him out and frighten the living daylights out of his wife so she flew toward the tower and ran up the spiral staircase.

Mr. Hornsby was beginning to come to and staggered toward the door just as his wife flung it open as hard as she could and hit him with tremendous force on the front of the head. Mr. Hornsby then spiraled out of the door and down the spiral staircase almost all the way to the bottom . . . But again, that didn't kill him.

Mrs. Hornsby ran down the staircase as fast as she could and saw that Mr. Hornsby had landed with his head up the stairs and his feet down the stairs. He was not moving, and to her, he looked as good as dead.

She leapt over him and ran outside to get the car, not thinking whether or not she could even get him into the car. When she got close to the tower door, she ran back inside and attempted to move her husband. She was relieved to hear his moans. The irony of this was that two days earlier she had told him to quit moaning about everything or she was going to leave him, but today his moans sounded like music to her ears.

She thought that she could lift him to his feet by grabbing him under his arms, but discovered the meaning of dead weight and could not lift him. She moved back down to his feet and grabbed his ankles and started pulling him down the stairs . . . Of course you know as well as I do what this did to his head . . . Bump, bump, bump, bump! And too this did not kill him.

Somehow she managed to get him into the car; perhaps it was pure adrenaline. She slammed the car into drive and showered gravel for a hundred feet. She sped down the road as fast as she could to get him to the hospital.

The road from the resort down to the main campus was very curvy and very bumpy and was covered with loose dirt and gravel. It was also used as the main route by very determined, very well fit, and somewhat insane runners. After all, who runs up a hill toward a lightning storm?

Unfortunately today, there were three running abreast, and when Mrs. Hornsby rounded a curve, there they were! Off the road and down the mountainside she careened . . . God bless the Hornsbys. Some say it was the most beautiful funeral that was ever given on the campus. Oh, by the way, the car *did not* explode! They almost never do.

Mr. Hornsby was the third caretaker of the resort to die on the job in less than seven years. This fact made it very difficult for the college to recruit a new caretaker. Barry's supervisor, who found out how cantankerous he was and was having the same problems with him as we had, recruited Barry to apply for the job. The supervisor wanted him gone any way that he could, because it was so difficult for anyone to be fired from this extremely liberal institution. The reasons for dismissal had to be horrific, but annoyance was not one of them.

The supervisor lobbied so hard for Barry to be put on the mountain that they hired him without even an interview.

So Barry went to his dream job while I remained at my "job" job . . . Now . . . *this really is bullshit!*

***

"Thud"

"What was that?"

"I don't know. Whatever it was, was loud!"

"It sounded like a monument fell off the truck!"

"You think ya ought to go see what it was?"

"Probably should."

"Let me know if we need to call an ambulance."

"I hope it was just a stone falling off the truck."

"Mmm-huh, I know that's right!"

It wasn't a stone. It did make a cloud of dust, whatever it was that hit the ground. Through the dust my brother could see a figure laboriously trying to rise from the ground. Of course there were only a couple of possibilities of who it could be and it wasn't Craig.

It was Scott, my nephew, who was pretty big. He had always wanted to work at the monument company. His mother was like my mother who was like many other mothers who did not want their sons taking dangerous jobs that don't pay so great.

During the first few days that he worked, when I went out to the cemetery with him, he was incessantly asking questions about why do you do this, why do you do that, blah blah blah blah blah.

I wanted to tell him that he would have to wait until I finished writing the manual for setting stones, but naturally, that would never be forthcoming. So I finally told him with a really horrible impression of a Chinese accent, "Ah, Grass-stomper, you must wait and see, for all will be exposed to you in time. Watch with eyes open, Grass Stomper, and you will know!"

It worked! He understood that I was not a gifted teacher, blessed with great verbosity, but I did explain things much better while I was in the process of completing the task.

Of course the monument business is not really that dangerous if one follows the rules. Scott tried to follow the rules, but his body had a mind of its own.

Craig was like a dancing hippopotamus who eventually got to where, unlike in the beginning, he could dance across a double grave that was entirely covered with trinkets without knocking a single one over. Conversely, it was obvious that if Scott accidentally stepped on a grave full of trinkets, he *could not* dance. He would just give up and tackle the ground, scattering trinkets like a small explosion!

What would happen was that when he stumbled or tripped, he looked like he was trying to run his way out of it and was either trying to make a shoulder tackle or a full on arm tackle as though he was trying to wrap his arms around the earth. I always wondered if he was trying to slow down or speed up the rotation of the earth depending on which direction he was galloping.

If he had played linebacker on a football team he would have probably been the leading tackler, provided that a teammate would stick his foot out at the precise moment, because he always accelerated immensely after tripping.

Once when we were trying to set a stone, he tripped over the maddock and spun out of control and went head first into a nine hundred-pound tombstone, knocking it over. I thought surely he would have had a concussion. Fortunately he didn't, but I believe the tombstone did.

Sometimes he tripped because he was trying to avoid tripping. Once, only seconds after we had replaced the glass on the sandblast booth, I heard a rumble and then a tremendous *THUD* and the shattering of glass. A small air hose was lying in the pathway leading to the inside of the shop, and while trying to avoid stepping on it, he got his foot caught in a loop and went flying into the sandblast booth!

When I turned around I saw that his right shoulder was firmly implanted into the sandblast curtain. He wasn't injured that time either. He never admitted that he was hurt, which is a good thing because we could not afford workman's comp. Of course that means that he was an officer of the corporation, being "vice president in charge of not getting hurt."

Naturally, after hearing a half dozen or so thuds in the course of six months, my sarcastic, satirical, ass-holish self had no other choice than to dub him "Sir Thud." Or "Thud," for short.

It was decided that maybe if Scott started doing the sandblasting that he would quit falling down. Okay, his body quit falling down; however, his psyche was another matter.

Part of the garb that he wore to sandblast in involved eye, ear, and lung protection. When the sandblaster is going full throttle and you're wearing all that stuff, you really shouldn't try to sing!

"What in the hell is that racket?" Dad demanded to know while he was sitting on the couch in the office.

"I believe that would be Scott trying to sing," I replied.

"Well, if that's singing I'm Albert Einstein! It sounds more like he's being castrated with a butter knife!" Dad said disdainfully.

"I told him he needed to tone it down a little bit . . . Evidently he can't hear shit!" Danny replied.

Dad got up from the couch and went to the medicine cabinet and took out a bottle of aspirin then went to the water cooler and got a cup of water. He went down to the shop, where Scott was still bellowing, and held out his hands to present the remedy.

Scott didn't see the aspirin and told Dad after removing his respirator, "Thanks, Norm, but I'm not thirsty."

Dad thrust the aspirin a little closer so that Scott could see it.

"I thought you might need this since you sounded like you are in so much pain!" Dad told him with a huge grin.

"All right! I get the hint."

It really hurt Scott's feelings; they went "thud" you might say. He really could sing, but with that garb on, he sounded like a member of the "Helen Keller Choir." He might have gotten the hint, but every once in a while when he was blasting he couldn't help himself. He would start up a song and then look around to see if anyone was listening and would slowly bring his volume down until it was just a barely audible hmm, hmm, hmm a-hmm, hmm.

Thud eventually quit thudding, but that didn't matter because everyone continued to call him Thud. Once he got to the point where the earth was no longer his enemy and he quit knocking over tombstones he really liked the job.

I remember it well. It was the sincerest of statements, and it sounded true, "I really love this job. Honestly, it is the best job I have ever had and I would love to stay here forever."

I told him that sounded good to me. The fact is, he didn't stay for a very long time. It wasn't the weather. The work was steady. He was doing a fine job. One might say that shit happens. In his particular case some *really weird shit happened!*

***

Polly Roper or Why Thud's Hair Went "Thud"

S cott quit. He didn't tell us why. We thought that it was because he had worked 'til dark one Saturday cutting death dates. Saturday work was always optional and that was the one thing that paid him well, but we thought maybe he felt some pressure and he just didn't want to do it anymore.

I tried to call him, but he would not talk to me. Dad tried to call him. My brother tried to call him. We couldn't get through so we asked Craig to call him. Craig didn't get through.

My ex-wife, his aunt, tried to call him. After a couple of weeks, she finally got through. She just simply told me that Scott was full of shit.

I told her that that was beside the point and could she please tell me what he said. She rolled her eyes and said that he might tell me if I went to visit him in person. In turn, I rolled my eyes because I was tired of playing games.

So I went to Scott's house and banged on the doors and I banged on the windows and I banged on the walls and I called his name. I saw the drape in his bedroom window gently close and I knew he was there.

"Scott! What in Sam Hill is going on? Why won't you answer your phone? Look, I know you're in there! All right! You leave me no choice! I'm calling your mother."

I saw his drapes waiver, probably from him slinging his bedroom door open. I could hear the thud of his footsteps coming to the front door. He slung it open and demanded to know what I wanted, but of course he knew what I wanted.

I was a little shocked at what I saw. Scott's hair appeared to be falling out and he was turning gray around the fringes. He was only thirty years old for crying out loud! I know he knew what I was looking at because he was tapping his foot at the rate of about two hundred beats a minute.

"Okay! So what do you want? What are you looking at? My hair? Cat got your tongue? Well! Say something."

"Uh . . . I don't know what to say. What happened to you?"

"Yeah . . . My hair's falling out! I'd just as soon that you not be here."

"Yeah well, if you weren't Cindy's nephew, I wouldn't be here. You know I had to talk everyone into hiring you in the first place, and at least you could give us an explanation as to why you haven't shown up for two weeks!"

After what seemed like an interminable pause, he let me in. He sat down on the edge of his favorite chair and beckoned me to sit also. He started wringing his hands and then reached up and rubbed his head, and when he looked at it, he saw that it was full of hair.

"See? It's coming out bad," he lamented.

"I do see . . . What do you think it could be?" I asked as I was thinking poison, drugs, cancer, maybe all of the above.

"I really don't know how to tell you . . . You won't believe me anyway."

"Come on! You know me better than that. You know that I've always been easy to talk to."

"You are so judgmental! You're going to laugh at what I have to say, I know you!"

"If you don't really want to tell me, then okay . . . I'll try to understand, but you're starting to piss me off!"

I wasn't really that pissed off. I didn't really give a damn, but I knew that due to his past respect for me, that it would be hard on him to think that I was. I waited in silence for another minute and gave up and started for the door.

"All right! I'll tell you, but you have to promise that you won't think I'm insane."

"I already think you're insane! So what's the difference? You're a Franklin, aren't you?"

"Do you remember the last day I worked?"

"Of course . . . It was the last day that you worked."

"Don't be so obtuse!"

"How can I? I don't even know what that is," I said stupidly.

"I saw a ghost," he said softly.

"Oh, well, is that all? You work in a cemetery. You're bound to see a ghost every once in a while."

"I'm serious . . . It was the ghost of a woman . . . She was very beautiful."

"Look, you were there close to dark. You had been working all day and you were probably dehydrated. I mean, I can't tell you how many times that I thought I saw someone out of the corner of my eye. You know I sometimes wonder if that's how angels appear . . . You just see them briefly and then they disappear, but really it's probably just an illusion."

"It was no illusion, Kev! I spoke to her and she spoke back!"

"Okay, so she spoke back. Was she translucent or something? You know, could you see through her, or was she floating about or changing shapes?"

"No! Look, it's hard to explain. I'll tell you how I know she was a ghost if you'll listen!" Scott said with daggers shooting from his eyes.

"Okay, I'll listen."

I listened. I have to admit that the hair stood up on the back of my neck. I never knew him to be such a good storyteller. I was always skeptical when people would tell me these kind of things, but really, I think that I was jealous that I had not had one of these experiences myself.

Scott was very convincing. He didn't hesitate nor did he stammer. As he spoke he stared straight ahead:

"The last date that I cut that Saturday was at Smith cemetery and it was nearly dark. When I finished cutting I suddenly had to pee really bad. So I walked over the hill away from the highway to find a bush and was startled by a young woman that was standing at a grave. She seemed to be lit up by some kind of reflected light. You know how the sun reflects off of stones and sometimes lights things up around them? Well, that's what I thought it was. Of course, then I couldn't pee, since she was standing right there. That's when I said hello to her. She said hello back in a very airy, very lovely voice. The strange part was that it didn't seem to register in my ears, but in my mind. I was beginning to feel cold at this point, and you know it was nearly ninety degrees that day, and even though the sun was going down, it was still hot and very muggy. At any rate she just stood there looking at me very lovingly I thought. Like an idiot, I asked her if she went there often, and she replied, 'Only once a year.' She was standing over a small flat stone and I noticed the date of death was June 11, 1997. That was exactly four years to the day! I tried to make small talk with her, but she didn't have a whole lot to say. I noticed that her hair was being gently blown, but all of it stayed in place, and I could tell that she didn't use hairspray, you know, when your hair blows in the wind it usually musses it a little. I suddenly realized that the wind wasn't even blowing! I also realized that even though she appeared to be standing in a reflected light, the sun was below the hillside. I told her after a couple of minutes that I needed to go clean the stone that I was working on and I had better leave before dark. She said that she understood and that she would not be able to stay much longer herself; she needed to try to find Madeleine. I asked her what her name was as I started to walk away and she said, 'Polly Roper.' I walked toward her to shake her hand and told her my name, but she appeared to move away from me without actually moving her legs. I really wasn't comprehending what was going on because I was completely mesmerized by her beauty. I smiled and told her that it was nice to meet her and I turned around to go back to finish up. I took about three or four steps and then turned around to ask her for her phone number but she was gone! I looked around to see if I could find her, but she was nowhere to be seen. I looked to see if there was a trail leading away from the cemetery, but as you know, that cemetery is surrounded by a barbed-wire fence, all except the entrance road. I walked back over to where she was standing and looked down at the small stone and noticed the name—it was Polly Roper! At first

I thought that maybe it was her mother by the same name, but the birth date was April 14, 1971. That would have made her twenty-six years old and I knew for certain it was not her mother's stone. That's how old the woman that I was talking to looked. The other thing that I didn't mention was that there was no car or bicycle or any other mode of transportation she could have used! What else was I to think? I knew that she had to be some kind of spirit or ghost or something! After that I don't really remember anything until I got home. I even forgot to pee until I got home!

I wasn't completely satisfied, so when Scott finished talking, I asked him a few questions. I asked him what she was wearing; I don't know why. (Okay, I confess, my prurient interests got the better of me and I was hoping that she was wearing some sort of chiffon nighty.) I know that she had long flowing blonde hair but I asked him what her features were like.

He told me that she was wearing a brown flannel long sleeve shirt, baggy blue jeans, and snake skin cowboy boots (not at all what I had ever imagined beautiful ghosts wearing, but at the same time I was somewhat turned on). The belt buckle she was wearing looked like two rattlesnakes intertwined and she was wearing a brooch that was shaped like a coiled rattlesnake. She was wearing earrings that looked like tiny spiders. Her hazel eyes were framed by thick brows and long lashes and were very piercing. She had high cheekbones and naturally full lips.

I listened intently to his answer and then I asked him plainly, "So, Scott, why would any of this make you quit? You know, it was hot that day and you might have been having heat stroke. Look, I'm not saying that you did not see a pretty woman, but why would she have to be a ghost? How do you know that your mind didn't play tricks on you?"

"I can't explain it. I've had heat stroke before and I've never hallucinated anything! You would have had to be there to know what I saw. It changed me, Uncle Kevin, and I know I can't go near a cemetery again!"

I always liked the idea that there might be ghosts, but even though I was completely into what Scott was telling me, I still didn't really believe him. A hundred different reasons for the apparition that Scott had seen went through my mind. Still, I wanted it to be true. I decided to check into this person named Polly Roper.

The first chance I got I called Harold Ramsey, the owner of the largest funeral home in Springdale, which was the funeral home that handled ninety percent of the burials in that county. It was also the funeral home that had been converted from a grocery store and where in the back, usually hidden by a set of double doors, up high were the words "Fresh Meats." Springdalers are a strange bunch and this only added to Mr. Ramsey's popularity. Several joked about being laid out in the produce department.

"Harold, I got a question for you."

"Sure, okay, what you got?"

"Did you do a funeral for a young lady named Polly Roper?"

He didn't even have to think about it. "Yes, I did . . . Why do you ask?" he asked as his demeanor got serious.

"Well, you know Scott? He quit after he said he saw her. I figured it was heat stroke."

Harold had to clear his throat before he could reply. "Yeah . . . He wouldn't be the first. I've heard of ten or fifteen people who have seen her standing over her grave. It's always right before dark on the anniversary of her death. Now who am I to say?"

"It was on the anniversary of her death all right, and it was right before dark, but I just can't help but believe that someone is pulling everybody's leg . . . Wait a minute! She's only been dead a few years! Have all these people seen her on the same day? I just don't believe there is any such thing as ghosts."

"Well, don't be so sure. I don't know if they all saw her at the same time or not. Seems strange, don't it? Well, there are a lot of strange things that can happen in this life! You know, people around here considered her a witch and she never tried to dispel any of those rumors . . . Anyway, somebody or somebodies killed her. They burned down her house, with her in it, and burned her little country store . . . killed all of her animals. I heard that she lived with goats in her house and tons of cats and an old lesbian named Madeleine. She had all kinds of pentagrams and talismans and tarot cards and everything you can think of, and a lot of folks were scared of her. To tell you the truth, I wasn't too keen on burying her myself."

"Pretty scary to me . . . But pisses me off . . . Why can't people just leave other people alone? Hey listen, I guess you couldn't have told what she was wearing, her being burned up and all."

"She wasn't burned up at all! She died of smoke inhalation. The coroner said she had a bump on her head so she must've been knocked out and then the fire was set, but it never actually got all the way to her. Nobody knows why they didn't just set fire to her bed to hide the evidence, 'cause that's where they found her . . . You know, she was so beautiful."

"So you could tell what she was wearing?"

"Yeah, I thought I said I could?"

"So what was she wearing?"

"Oh, well . . . She was wearing a plaid shirt and some baggy blue jeans and . . . I don't know, maybe some earrings that looked like spiders or something."

"I get the gist of it. Anyway, thanks for the info. Maybe Scott's not crazy. I think maybe next June I'll go out to Smith cemetery and see if maybe I can find that lady."

"You better be careful! Don't count out the fact that there might be demons and black magic. Don't ever take that stuff lightly!"

About a month later, Craig and I went to Smith cemetery to set a stone. I decided to go look for Polly Roper's tombstone. I walked all over the cemetery and could not find that stone anywhere! I wondered if someone might have removed it, so I started looking for a grave with a missing stone and didn't find that either.

I asked Craig to see if he could find it, but he couldn't either. Needless to say, we were both puzzled. Was it possible that Scott was at a different cemetery?

I called Harold and confirmed that he had buried Polly Roper in Smith cemetery. He told me that she was buried in front of da, da, da and next to de, de, de, which was exactly where I was standing and there was no grave!

I looked at Craig and told him what Harold said. Don't laugh, but Craig looked like he had seen a ghost! Needless to say, we hurried up and got the hell out of there!

I had goose bumps and my hair stood on end all the way back to the shop. Craig and I didn't say a damn thing to each other until we got back.

"Maybe we were on the wrong side of the cemetery from what Harold was telling us," Craig said.

"I don't think there would have been two different sets of people with the same name in such a small cemetery."

"I didn't think of that."

"I don't know what to think . . . It's just weird. How could we have missed her grave? We both looked everywhere and then Harold told us who she was buried next to, which is exactly where we were standing."

"I don't know about you, but I would just as soon not go back to that cemetery," Craig said emphatically.

"I don't know! I might go back there tonight!"

"You're nuts!"

"Yep, I'm trying to quit being such a stick in the mud," I said as I was thinking about the time that Bobby and I broke into that mausoleum. What! Didn't I tell you about that? Well, don't worry. I'll get to it.

I didn't go back that night, but I kept thinking about that day. There was a burning question that I needed answered. Was Polly Roper a figment of everyone's imagination or was she just a big joke that people like Harold were having fun with? Of course Thud wouldn't have had his hair to fall out just to be in on a joke!

It was sometime in August that I decided to take another trip to Smith cemetery. It was after work on a weekday, and after I had tidied a few things up, I knew that it would be almost dusk when I got there. I sort of planned it that way, thinking maybe Ghost Polly visited on other days.

The closer I got to the cemetery, the more I felt this electric current going through me. I tried to calm down but it was difficult. The sun was just beginning to go down behind the far trees. I felt a little disappointed when I entered the cemetery and there was no Polly.

I circled around the entire cemetery, and as expected, I didn't see anyone or anything out of the ordinary. I decided to park at the bottom of the hill and read the newspaper that I brought along, just to give it a few more minutes before heading home.

The evening was still very warm and I could have used the air conditioner, but in order to save gas, I turned off the engine and rolled down the window. As I was reading the paper it began to quiver as though it was blowing in the breeze, but there was no breeze!

Instinctively, I looked in the direction where Polly Roper was allegedly buried. Shocked I was at the sight of a very beautiful woman. Yes, she was hauntingly beautiful. Is this Thud's ghost? I wondered. Well, let me tell you, at that particular moment, I was not about to get out of my truck to find out! I was having difficulty breathing, but then suddenly, I saw that the woman was looking lovingly at me, and strangely enough, I calmed down.

She gave a gentle wave that seemed to beckon for me to come near her. I hesitantly got out of my truck and moved toward her. When I got close enough, I noticed that she was standing over the very grave that Craig and I obviously overlooked. The little marker was right where it should've been, but oddly enough, it did not say June 11; it said August 17, 1997. I was standing there on the anniversary of Ms. Polly Roper's death. Scott must have been confused; it wasn't just his body that went thud!

I looked at the woman who was standing there and noticed that she was wearing the clothes that Scott had described, including the earrings, boots, belt, and brooch. I introduced myself and she returned the courtesy and told me that her name was Molly Roper.

"So your name isn't Polly!" I said joyously with a little relief thrown in.

"Oh goodness no! Polly was my twin sister. I always come here on the anniversary of her murder and I always wear the same outfit that she had on when she died."

"I see! But my nephew was just here a couple of months ago and said that he was here on the anniversary of her death and that he saw you standing here and that your name was Polly."

"Yes, I was here two months ago and I remember your nephew, and yes, I told him my name was Polly because I wondered if he was going to ask me out, just the way he looked at me, you know . . . I know it was a cruel trick, but sometimes it's hard to resist," she said with a cynical grin.

I told her of how Craig and I were looking for Polly's grave and couldn't find it, and I swore to her that we had stood right where we were standing now and wondered if someone had moved her from somewhere else.

"Well, I declare! No, it's always been right here, since August of 1997. Maybe the sun was in your eyes or something."

"Maybe it was!"

After a couple of more minutes, I told her I needed to get on home and she concurred that she should do the same. We shook hands and it was obvious to me that she was flesh and blood and not a ghost. She said that she was going to stay a few more minutes to reflect a little bit and bid me farewell.

When I got to my truck, I backed it into the cemetery a little to turn around and looked in the mirror and did not see her. This startled me slightly to begin with, so I turned around and saw that she was still standing there. I figured that the mirror was just pointing the wrong way and even though I adjusted it, I could not get her to come into view.

As I drove away, I looked back to get another glimpse of her but did not see her. I decided to drive back around the cemetery and still did not see her, and just like Scott, I realized that I never heard a car pull up, or anything else, as I was sitting there in my truck!

That night I couldn't sleep. I had cold chills one minute; feverish the next. I took my temperature; it was normal. I felt like a string of barbed wire caught in a Bush-hog. Was I losing my mind? We had a stone going to Springdale the next day; a visit to Harold Ramsey's funeral home would be on the agenda.

The next day Craig and I went into the funeral home and met with Harold. I told him that I met Polly Roper's twin sister, Molly.

"She didn't have a twin sister," Harold said adamantly.

"Are you sure?" I asked a little nervously. "Do you think maybe someone was pretending to be her twin?"

"I guess that's possible," he answered with a twinkle in his eye. "Hey, I've got a picture of Polly that was taken about two weeks before she was murdered. You wanna see it?"

Of course I wanted to see it . . . I saw it. It looked just like Molly, down to the tiny mole on the left side of her neck! My brain suddenly felt like a whole roll of barbed wire caught in a Bush-hog.

"Listen, there's something else. What was the exact day that she died?"

"Well, now, let's see," he said as he thumbed through her file. "She died on December 2, 1997 . . ."

That explained the long-sleeve flannel shirt and baggy blue jeans . . . My hair was already thin. I began to hope like hell that it didn't get any thinner!

***

Just a Little Information
or a Dose of Reality

Understand one thing: the monument business is hard. The granite is hard. The work is hard. The customers are hard. The people who run the cemeteries are hard. The trip to Elberton is hard. The heads of the people who work in the business are hard. Making money is hard. Tell me something in the monument business that isn't hard!

Okay, so it sounds like I'm whining. At the end of the day, you're covered with dust. You try to take the air hose and blow it off, but you never get it all.

You get home and all the sand and dust that you got in your clothes that day and what you didn't get off with the air blower winds up on your floor. So why not take your clothes off outside? What if you couldn't have afforded a house where you could take your clothes off outside and the neighbors wouldn't see you?

You wake up in the middle of the night, you've had your shower so you should be clean, and a little particle of sand that you didn't get off, which was probably stuck in a hair follicle in your eyebrow, migrates its way down, right into your eye. Every time you blink, that little particle rolls around scratching your cornea.

So you've worn a respirator all day and your nose breaks out and irritates the hell out of you, so the next day you don't wear the respirator and your nostrils build up with boogers from hell! So you try to dig them out, and you start pulling on one that appears to have an umbilical cord attached to it and you pull that thing out two or three inches and the cord is still attached and you're afraid just to yank it, in case you bleed to death, so you think you might ought to cut it and tie it off!

You've asked your customer if the grave, which they just bought their tombstone for, is easy to get to and they reply, "Oh yes, you can back right to it and the ground is flat." We are always suspicious of this statement because they say "flat" and not "level."

And you get to the cemetery . . . The f——ing grave is up a hardly flat (that is to say, very bumpy), 45 percent slope, and in the middle of a whole bunch of other graves that have walls around them and concrete angels and little statues of puppy dogs and occasionally a Mountain Dew bottle or two and you *could* back your truck up to it except even a four-wheel drive keeps spinning out in the loose chert.

So what do you do? You try to find a place up above it, but you can't find one. Well, actually you can find one, but it's a half a mile away. So you call the shop and tell them to send somebody to help push the hand trucks up the hill.

By the time your help arrives, you've already dug out for the footer and you've carried four eighty-pound bags of concrete mix up the hill 225 feet away from the truck. You've gotten the hand trucks off the truck and you already have the base on them when your help arrives.

The help arrives and they always say, "What! You mean y'all couldn't get that base up that little bitty hill?"

So we want to slug him, but what's the point? So we start pushing the base up the hill and the help, which just arrived, starts huffing and puffing a third of the way up and wants to stop!

"So I guess you understand why we didn't start without you?"

Hugh! Hugh! Hugh! That's how the "fresh" help sounds because the "fresh" help can't breathe, and fortunately, he also can't reply with anything smart-aleck. So we wait it out until he quits, calling "Hugh" and we start pushing the base up the hill again.

The guy with the hand trucks can't let go or the two who are pushing will get the shit knocked out of them and the base might get broken to boot!

So you finally get the base to the hole and you flip it over on to boards. Then you raise one end up with a bar or a stout shovel and you pull the board out. Then you raise the other end up and then pull that board out. Then you level it. Then you go back down the hill and get the die. (The top part that has the lettering on it is called a die.)

The die, being taller than the base in relation to the hand trucks, feels much heavier. The guy pulling the hand trucks struggles to keep it balanced. Push down too much on the handles and he might lose his footing. Let up too much on the handles and a tiny little footstone or root or anything else might cause the stone to tip on over onto the pushers. Go up the hill at the wrong angle and the stone might start to slide off of the hand trucks, especially if you hit a hole.

So you get back to the shop, exhausted, and invariably there's somebody there, whose name I won't mention, will always ask, "What took y'all so long?"

So that's a day in the cemetery, but what about in the shop? Well, you hook a stone up to the bridge crane and you put it in the layout room. If it's dry enough, you put the stencil on it. Until the last decade or so everyone cut stencil by hand; now a lot of companies use a stencil machine.

So how do you make the stencil? The stencil comes in rolls and you unroll enough to cover what you want to put on the stone. After you would lay out the stone with the design work and lettering, you would take an X-Acto knife and cut out the rubber and whatever you pull out creates the stencil and then the stone is sandblasted down.

Used to, when it was really cold, you would have to try to warm the stone up so that you could even cut the stencil and you would constantly have to sharpen your knife. In fact around World War II, the stencil did not come in rolls because of the war effort, so you would have to make it yourself with this rubbery stuff that you put in a pot and cooked it down on a stove and then you had to take a paintbrush and paint it onto your stone and let it cool all night so that you could cut the next day. So in effect, you would have to get as many stones as you had room for to put the goo on, so that you could do more than one the next day.

When you put the stone in the sandblaster and start sandblasting, you have to be very careful not to hold the sand in one spot for too long or it will burn the shit out of the stencil and then you've got to put another stone in the layout room and start all over.

Of course you also have to deal with equipment breaking down and it never picks a good time. We always hold our breath around Christmas time and Mother's Day and Easter and all those days that people want to have their stone up for. One day, when we missed putting a stone up by Mother's Day (but got it up the day after), I made the comment to look at it this way, "We've gotten it up a year early!"

The customer was not amused. What can I say? I have ADD, and sometimes I say things that I'm thinking. It's almost as bad as Tourette's syndrome, but at least I don't string out a bunch of profanity.

And then of course you know what I've said about the pay. Sometimes it's not too bad. But then a lot of the time it sucks! So why do I keep doing this job? Because it is hard and that's the way that I pay homage to my grandfather and my father. In reality, I wouldn't have it any other way. No disrespect to women or the marines. This is why we say, "The few, the proud, the monument men!"

***

Henry Starts to Work at the Monument Company

"I was the valedictorian of my class," said the new guy.

I looked at Craig . . . Him at me. We rolled our eyes simultaneously . . . Didn't know it was going to become such a habit.

"Really? What school did you go to?" I asked, trying not to laugh.

"I went to Juniper Crag," he answered a little cockily.

Juniper Crag is in Alabama, twenty-five miles from Hamburg, where one of the smartest men I know went to school, so because of this, I had no prejudice toward it, but at the same time one of the smartest men I know never said how smart he was, nor did he ever say that, in essence, he was a rocket scientist, which he was, but our esteemed companion definitely was not.

"Well, there aren't that many people in Juniper Crag," I chided. "What did you do, sneak everybody a joint before test time?"

"Whatayoumean?" asked New Guy.

"Did you get everybody stoned so you would have the highest grades?"

"Did you ride the little short bus to school?" Craig scoffed.

"What is a back-a-lick-torian anyway?" I joked.

"I said VALedictorian!" retorted New Guy.

"Is that something *special?*" asked Craig.

"That's why he rode the short bus to school," I mused.

We hit a nerve with the newbie but what did he expect with such a preposterously pretentious comment? After all, he had come to work in a business that, for him at least, would mainly require guts, grit, and gusto for working in the dirt. There we were, riding down an old country road to a cemetery and the first thing he said was, "I was the valedictorian of my class."

It's not that digging a hole is as easy as it looks. Certainly any ol' rocket scientist can dig one with a little instruction, but really, how much education did he think he needed? Perhaps he thought he could tell us how to do our job. I figured out later that he just liked to talk and he needed validation from time to time.

Get the picture: he was a dumpy little guy with close to thirty trips around the sun on our bountiful little orb. He had long blonde hair pulled into a ponytail. He wore very thick glasses and a camouflage hat. He had a pouty sort of mouth due to his slight under-bite.

It was obvious that his scholastic achievement had not created any type of advantage toward the great "American Dream." His name was Carl Hibbet. His father's name was Leroy Hibbet, pronounced Lee Ro e. Now you have to say it fast or it won't come out right. No, it's more like Lee Raw' e. Oh, forget it. If you aren't a southerner, you'll never get it.

I would later call him "Henry," not to make fun but because I kept calling him "Craig." Well, okay, he did look more like a Henry anyway. I mean . . . you remember the old "Henry" comic strip? Maybe you should Google it. That's who he looked like.

Of course, as you already discovered, we already had a Craig who was sitting against the passenger side door with Carl sitting in the middle on this fine summer day with me driving to our daily battle with the graveyard. It was of great comfort to know that we had such a mental giant on board!

For a few days after he began working with us, when I needed him to do something. I would call Cr—Carl until I got so frustrated with it that I renamed him Henry. He didn't like it to begin with. I convinced him that, to avoid confusion, "Henry" was as good a name as any.

"Why do you keep calling me 'Henry'?"

"What difference does it make?"

"My name isn't Henry. It's Carl!"

"Henry has a nice ring to it. Henry Hibbet, Henry Hibbet. Carl Hibbet, Carl Hibbet. Sounds like you're saying Cahribbet . . . like a frog!"

"I still don't like it. You aren't showing any respect for my deddy!"

Of course not respecting a southern boy's "deddy" is the equivalent of throwing down the gauntlet. The vein in the Frankenstein monster's head didn't have anything on the vein popping out of Henry's head. His face turned as crimson as a University of Alabama football helmet.

I knew that I had to abandon my unabashed penchant for revelry. Since he was already showing promise as a good worker, I eased him out of his quandary by delivering what I thought was a brilliant oratory worthy of Dr. Phil himself.

"Get over it!"

Have you ever seen goat eyes? Well, that's what I got from Henry. Some animals, cows for instance, have a sweet, innocent look that belies the fact that most of us will devour a couple of dozen of them in our lifetime. Goats have a look that is pure evil. "You're not gonna eat me motherfucker. I'll pluck your heart right out!" I'm pretty sure that's what the Devil has . . . goat eyes. That look coming from a human being is mortifying enough to freeze you in your tracks.

I knew that it was time to regain an air of professionalism so I gave him a halfway honest account with a genuine smile to frame it with.

"Okay, I'll tell you why I call you Henry. Haven't you noticed that every time I call your name I say Cr-Carl? 'Cr-ah shit Carl, hand me that thing' . . . 'Cr-Carl' . . . you know."

"Wuh yeah. I just thought you had a speech impediment."

"No! I keep screwing up and keep wanting to call you 'Craig,' so it's just easier to call you Henry."

"Oh! Okay. I was just wonderin," he said with a tone of forgiveness.

So we went back to work and his name was henceforth "Henry." He got so used to it that months later, he referred to his very own little boy as Henry Junior.

***

Beauty Abounds

"This is a great job when you get right down to it," Henry said as he was driving to the cemetery.

"I guess," said I. The thought of it made me tired.

"No, really it is. You get to be outside. You get to go to places you didn't know existed. When you're in the cemetery, nobody hardly bothers you."

"You know, you are right, even though it's a major pain in the ass, but as far as no one bothering you, well, you just ain't been in the business long enough."

"What do you mean?"

"Well, for example, one day my dad and I went to this cemetery out in the country to set some coping [low granite wall] and we were going to join it to another lot, and before we could finish it, this redneck comes up and says, 'If ya'll don't move that right now, I'll get my shotgun and blow your fucking heads off.' As you can imagine, Dad and I were pretty shocked, so Dad tried to convince him that it would benefit him just as much as it would the lady we were setting it for, because, otherwise, grass would grow in between the two lots. But the guy got even redder and started for his truck."

"What did ya'll do?"

"We moved it and had to go get another piece."

"I'd a gotten my gun and we'd a dueled it out right then and there!"

"A duel in the cemetery? Are you out of your mind?"

"You have to stand up for yourself sometimes."

"I didn't have a gun! I still don't have a gun!"

"You don't have a gun? Man, I've got, like twenty. I've got fifteen or twenty knives and a foot locker full of ammo."

"What in the heck can you do with that many guns?"

"I don't know, I just like 'em . . . I mean I go out and shoot, but it gets dang expensive."

"You take twenty guns out at one time!?"

"Nah . . . well, sometimes."

"Man! I couldn't stand the noise. What do the neighbors say?"

"Well, I don't have many and they're usually out there with me. Say, what's the matter? Are you one of them bleedin' heart lib'rals? You want to take away my rights to own firearms?"

"No, I'm not anti-gun or anything. I'm anti-noise."

"How'd we get on the subject of guns any-how?"

"Some redneck wanted to shoot us."

"Oh yeah," he said in a fading voice. "I'd a shot him first."

"I didn't have a gun."

"You said that."

"You know, don't you, that guns are just an extension of your penis."

"Ah! Now! You can't be serious! I don't get any sexual experience out of my gun."

I don't know why he said "experience." Maybe he meant "expression," or did he think about "experiencing it" and just never got around to it?

"Maybe not, but I bet you get some kind of euphoria out of it. What happens when you reach climax?" I asked.

"What kind? You mean sex?"

"Yeah, I mean sexual climax."

"Well, I usually shoot off . . . I get what you're saying now . . . That's pretty dang funny!" He laughed.

"That's right. When you fire that gun, you're just ejaculating bullets," I said sarcastically.

On we rode to the cemetery, and when we arrived at this particular one, I noticed a car parked on the center drive, and according to Murphy's law, which I adapted to my own version, called Murphy's Monumental Law, I knew this car was parked exactly where we needed to be to set the tombstone, but still we would walk around, looking everywhere else first and then fifteen minutes later, we'd come back to the place where we knew to look to start with.

Even though I knew the fundamentals of said law, I had a difficult time practicing them, so I would always become a little agitated that my schizophrenic alter ego would over-ride my conscious self that drove the truck. Agitation over the effect of this law was also one of its axioms.

As we drove farther into the cemetery, Pleasant Something or other, I saw an unmarked grave that proved my suspicions. Higher up the hill and a little to the left of the unmarked grave was a woman bent over a floral arrangement trying to straighten it. I must say that I couldn't help but notice her very large ass.

As we pulled in closer to her car, she raised and turned to watch us. She began staring at us with one of those "bitch" glares as though she was wondering whether she needed to run or give in to a couple of mad rapist who had the name of their company, their phone number, and their address right on the side of their truck! I've seen weathered old women rush with lightning speed to their cars on numerous occasions, as soon as I've parked the truck, so their reactions were never a surprise, but it was always irritating to see them run.

Whenever I would get out of the truck, on those occasions, I would turn and look at the door to make sure we had not mistakenly written "Hamburg Monument Co. & Rape Service . . . Purveyors of fine rapes . . . No job too big or small." Well, anyway, there she was staring and what do you know! It was Holly Hidowski!

Who the hell is Holly Hidowski, you ask. You remember! She was the very first semi-adult girl to ever dump me, that's who! Talk about inflation! It applied to her ass, that's for sure, and it gave me no satisfaction to see her in her new form.

I always had the comfort of knowing that, at least, I had been dumped by a real goddess and that if I had trouble performing in a current relationship I could return, in my mind, to the days of yore and could Glory Hallelujah once more. But damn! It was ruined forever. It was such a shock that I retreated into denial for a moment, but when she realized who I was, she looked almost ecstatic.

She waddled down the hill with her hand extended to shake mine, but as I reached for hers, she withdrew hers and said, "Oh, forget a shake. Give me a hug!"

Did she think she was doing me a favor? Perhaps she did because, as soon as we hugged, the memory of her gloriously athletic body was zapped from my databank and replaced by Holy BigCowski! That was all I could think of for the next two weeks, which convinced me that I was irretrievably damaged. My hard drive was turned into a floppy disc, causing a total system failure, requiring me to trash the whole old self and reconfigure a new one.

All that wasted space! Compared to her now, I looked like Cary Grant, sort of. Well, so there we were exchanging histories and all, and I couldn't wait for her to leave, but nooo . . . She kept talking and telling, and I could tell Henry was amused and taking every bit in—to use against me at a later date.

The only thing she didn't tell was that she had actually dumped me for a man twice her age who had a "real job" who knew more about making love than I would ever know and that he could give her everything that I couldn't (including the ass of a wildebeest). When she finally did leave, I asked Henry if he had one of his guns.

It almost surprised me when he pulled one out, but then again, I remembered who I was with.

"What was that all about? Did you really date her?"

"Yes, I did, but man has she changed," I said meekly.

Henry gave a hardy laugh and said in a tuneful voice, "Yeah, I bet!"

"No, really she used to be gorgeous."

"Mm-huh."

"I'll bring pictures."

"What? Out of a magazine?"

"No, you'll see."

"Okay, yeah, I believe you."

"You'll see . . . all right let's get to work."

"Go go go. Gimme dat shovel," he chortled.

Thirty minutes into the job, I remembered tearfully, almost, that my wife had burned all those glorious pictures of Holly (that I obviously had not hidden so well), after I—one time, and one time only—had said innocently—in my view—barely audible, "Holly, oh Ho . . ." You get the picture.

So we sweated and we grunted and we set our stone and all the while I was thinking of Holly and I didn't want to, but she was there in my mind, haunting me and reconfiguring back and forth from the then Holly to the now Holly, which discombobulated my brain even worse.

Henry got me out of my funk with his laughter and the statement that I'd heard something similar before.

"You know? It's stuff like this that makes me really like this job. I wouldn't mind staying here forever . . ."

Henry Changes His Mind and That Ain't All

"Okay, we're ready to go," stated Henry proudly.

"Have you got everything you need?" I asked.

"Yeah, I think so," answered Henry.

"Where's the vase?" I asked.

"Oh, I don't guess I do have everything!"

"I guess you better get it."

He got it.

"Have you got the footstone?"

"Ugh . . . Heck, guess I better get that too!"

I picked up the setting compound and the flat-ended shovel and put them on the truck.

"Looks like I forgot that too!"

"Yeah . . . Where's the water?"

"I think Craig has it."

"Craig's across the street cleaning up the stone y'all set yesterday . . . That's the other thing . . . Why didn't y'all clean it up yesterday? That old lady was really pissed off when she went up there last evening."

"Well, Craig said it wasn't that bad, and besides, he said it was going to rain and that would clean it up."

"It didn't rain, did it? I told you not to listen to everything Craig said. I told you that if something needed doing then do it!"

"Yeah, I know. I won't let it happen again," Henry said with his goofy grin.

Sometimes I would get a little miffed at the pair, but Henry's goofy grin almost always diffused my "miffedness." Well, except the time that when a very distraught young lady who had just lost her sister was showing Craig and him all of her family member's stones who had died within the last three years and he joked, "Gee, y'all are trying to kill off all y'all's family!"

We almost fired him, but we got over it and figured where else were we going to get a former valedictorian. We always joked that his IQ was so high that it got in his way. At any rate he was never going to be in anyone's PR department.

"So is there anything else you're missing?"

"I don't think so . . . Wait! We don't have any concrete on the truck!"

Hoorah! Maybe there is hope for the human race . . . Or at least Henry.

Craig got back in a little bit and all three of us double-checked the truck and finally everything was in order and ready to go. I had one last set of instructions and I was very explicit.

"Now, the cemetery you are going to is out in the boonies. You're going to get into Alabama and go to the top of Cloud Mountain, and when you get to county road 66, you're going to turn left and go about four miles. When you come to county road 69, you are going to turn right and go about two miles. Right about there is a very sharp right turn, and you better slow down all the way 'cause the cemetery is right there on the right. There's a dirt drive with a bunch of mailboxes and there used to be a gate across it. I don't know if it is still there, but if it is, do not go through that gate. I'm not kidding! Do not go through that gate! That is a compound that is occupied by a bunch of lesbians. And they're not the kind you see in the porno movies either. These are all a bunch of very masculine bull dikes who really hate men. According to someone, they cut a guy's balls off because he got too close to their compound."

"Ah, now you've done it! That's the first thing Henry's gonna do is go straight to that compound!" chortled Craig.

"Hell no! You're not gonna see me go to that compound! I'm sort of fond of my balls."

"Glad you are . . . You're wife probably can't stand the sight of them . . . If she can even find them!" Craig ribbed him again.

"Ha-ha . . . ," Henry returned ineffectually. Ten miles down the road he might come up with a retort.

"All right, guys! Get going . . . Now listen, the stone goes next to a double stone that has the last name Avery . . . It's right there on the contract . . . Bill and Joyce Avery. You shouldn't have any trouble finding it, but if you have to call somebody, you're going to have to go find a signal because you're pretty much out of the zone right there. Okay, y'all are gonna be gone a while . . . Better stop at Bojangle's."

After the boys went through Bojangle's and were back on the highway, Henry asked Craig, "How come we never get any money to buy our food when we go out? Seems like if we're gonna be gone this long that they'd at least pay us for our food and drink."

Craig rolled his eyes as he took a bite of a Bo Round. What he never told Henry was that Danny always handed him $10 apiece when they were going to be gone a long time. Naturally that money was for food. By this time Craig had pocketed about $200 that was earmarked for Henry's part.

"I think I'm gonna say somethin' to them," said Henry.

"Nah, that's okay. I'll say something to them by god! After all I am kin."

While shaking his head and shoulders in unity with his brethren, Henry chortled, "You all right, Craig! Think it'll do any good?"

"I doubt it . . . They're a bunch of stingy bastards. We'll see though."

Henry raised his cup to Craig in salutations. Craig just rolled his eyes and drove on.

The way to Cloud Mountain was always a pretty drive and Craig was enjoying the silence when Henry broke it. He couldn't help it. That was just the way he was. Craig turned on the radio, but Henry didn't get the hint.

"Do you know how to make a muhlotif cocktail?" asked Henry.

"A what?"

"A muhlotif cocktail."

"What in the hell is a muhlotif cocktail?"

"You know, it's a firebomb that you throw."

"You mean a Molotov cocktail?"

"Naw, I'm pretty sure it's muhlotif cocktail."

"Henry! You're full of shit. It's Molotov . . . It's named after a Russian politician who was part of the Bolshevik revolution."

"What the heck is a Bolshevik?"

"I thought you said that you were the valedictorian of your class! What kind of history did you study? The history of women's underwear?"

"That's not funny . . . Okay, you win. I just say things the way they're spelled."

"You're not though! It's not spelled muhlotif . . . It's spelled Molotov. M-O-L-O-T-O-V! Mah-lah-tov," reiterated Craig.

"Can we quit talking about this now?"

How did you know that Craig rolled his eyes? Indeed, he did as he reached for the radio and turned it up. Henry didn't get the message and kept talking. Craig reached for the radio again and turned it up some more.

After a couple of more times and the speakers becoming very distorted, almost blown, Henry shut up. Craig waited a couple of miles before turning the radio down, and when he did, Henry started talking again.

"Will you *please-shut-up*! I'm trying to drive!" Craig finally shouted over the radio.

"Why didn't you just say so?"

"You mean you couldn't figure out why I kept turning the radio up? Geez Louise, Henry you're such a moron!"

"Well, you don't have to get personal . . . If you start to fall asleep behind the wheel, I'm not going to wake you up!"

"Fine! I'm about to drive us off the road anyway because you drive me crazy!"

"I said okay! I'll shut up!"

So Henry shut up the rest of the way to Cloud Mountain. He was determined not to say anything, and even when Craig asked what was the number of the first county road they had to turn on, he didn't respond.

"Suit yourself, but business is business and talking about bull-shit things is not business. So which road is it?"

"All right! County Road 66 . . . Satisfied?"

So they turned left on to County Road 66 and drove about four miles until they got to County Road 69. After they turned, Henry asked, "Do you reckon those lesbians might have gotten the county to name it '69' on purpose?"

"I don't know, they might have? Seems appropriate, doesn't it?"

"Yeah, I bet they're up there doing it right now!" Henry said with a maniacal laugh.

"They might be, but you don't need to try to see if they are . . . Better stay close to the truck when we set that stone!"

"Oh, don't you worry! I'll make sure the stones are well protected!"

As hard as he might, Craig tried not to roll his eyes, but he did anyway. He was afraid that Henry was going to send him to the emergency room with an uncontrollable eye roll. How in the hell could he explain that to the doctor?

They got to the curve in the road, and sure enough, if they had not slowed way down, they would have missed the cemetery. The mailboxes to the lesbian compound were set back off the road just outside a closed gate and the cemetery was in the left corner of County Road 69 and the driveway.

Craig pulled the truck into the cemetery as quietly as he could. Even though they had official business to be there, he did not want to alert a bunch of militant lesbians and have them come snooping around.

Both got out and quickly found the grave, mainly because there was only one fresh one to be found and the Avery stone was right next to it.

Fortunately they were able to back the truck right up to it and quickly start to work. Of course Henry couldn't work without talking, so while Henry was talking, Craig lined it off and marked where to dig and got started.

While Craig was digging, Henry kept talking while he was getting all of the "condiments" necessary to set a tombstone. Craig wasn't listening to him and would just answer with a "yep" there and again.

The hole was finished and the concrete went in, followed by the base. Then Henry started doing the pee dance.

"I've really got to pee!" cried Henry.

"Well, you're just gonna have to wait. We'll finish this stone first and then we'll get in the truck and drive down the road and then you can get out and pee . . . But not before!"

"But I can't wait! It was that extra large sweet tea I drank and probably those three cups of coffee I had before I got to work!"

"Good god, Henry! You probably had to go before we even got here! Why didn't you tell me?"

"I figured I could hold it 'til we got here," Henry said with a sly grin.

"You did it on purpose, didn't you? You want to take a walk through the woods, don't you?"

"No, I didn't do it on purpose. I can't help what my bladder does! Can you?"

"Obviously better than you can," Craig replied angrily.

"Just to show you, I'll go across the street over there."

"All right then, go! Hurry back. I don't want to stay here all day. I'm already getting the creeps."

So Henry shuffled on across the road, which was how he ran, with his feet barely clearing the ground. Craig watched to make sure that he went into the woods, and when Henry disappeared, he went back to work.

Henry could still see Craig and headed west to go back across the road out of sight. Craig had looked at his watch and saw that it was time for his favorite radio program and turned on the satellite radio, which meant that he could not hear Henry rustling through the woods.

Henry could see the compound that was still a couple of hundred yards away so he slowed his approach and would get behind a large tree to make sure the coast was clear and then he would shuffle from tree to tree. When he got to within fifty yards, his bladder started to rebel.

He couldn't hold it any longer so he turned around and whipped it out and closed his eyes and let out a very slow sigh and was so relieved that he did not notice the approaching figures.

When he finished, he opened his eyes and was greatly frightened by the sight of two fugitive linebackers, both of them holding very menacing knives! Of course they were women; you know, the kind of women who don't like men, and they were very large and obviously very powerful.

Henry quickly zipped up and reached behind for his gun that was normally stuck in his belt. It wasn't there! Where the hell was it?

The men haters saw their opportunity and pounced on him very quickly. They stuffed a rag in his mouth before he could let out a yell and dragged him out of the woods into their compound.

In the meantime Craig was getting irritated because Henry should have finished by now. He kept looking up to see if Henry was coming out of the woods. You well know that he was getting very suspicious by now. After all, Henry was already gone long enough to empty twenty-five gallons of pee, but he then remembered the time that Henry fell off the truck, in slow motion, and it took what seemed like two minutes before he hit the ground!

"Henry! Where the hell are you? Hurry up! I'm ready to get out of here!"

Craig said to hell with it and finished up the stone himself. He sealed it, re-measured it, cleaned it, and put all the stuff back on the truck and was ready to go. This took about twenty minutes.

He thought about just leaving. He didn't really care how it looked to everybody. Well . . . What about the wife? He loved his wife. It wouldn't look too good to her. Better go find the son of a bitch.

Craig also carried a gun and was not averse to pulling it out. He went into the woods with his eyes wide open and his gun drawn. His intensity overcame his propensity to trip and he managed to traipse through the woods with barely a sound.

It took him several minutes to reach the enclave of surly slurpers, and when he got close enough, he carefully surveyed the area and noticed no-one outside. There appeared to be a main house, probably a gathering place, which was surrounded by several small cabins.

Craig dodged and ducked his way toward the larger house and worked his way to behind a bush that was in front of a window. He could hear several voices and could hear Henry, who had a higher pitched voice than the others, trying to coax his way out of a bad situation.

Henry was a simpleton in a way, and it was no surprise that he was trying to use a little humor and a little charm to get his way out of his conundrum.

Craig looked in the window and instantly recoiled in horror! They had Henry sitting in a chair, stripped down to his boxers with his ponytail taken down and his hands tied behind his back.

"Oh my god! He looks like one of them!" Craig said to himself.

It was his stringy blonde hair in need of washing, his smooth baby face with a hint of whiskers on his upper lip, his smooth hairless body . . . and . . . Oh my god! . . . Extreme man boobs!

Craig forced himself to look again. One of the women appeared to be licking her lips. He thought about busting his way in with his gun drawn, but when he checked it, he realized that he had left the clip in his jacket. He didn't think it would be too effective clicking an empty gun or a giant man going "bang bang bang bang!" in front of a bunch of bloodthirsty lesbians. Hardly!

Even if he had a loaded gun, he knew that he didn't want to run a quarter mile down a dirt road with a near-naked man with a bunch of angry lesbians in hot pursuit. So he took off to the truck alone and was no longer the dancing hippopotamus, but more like an overweight gazelle.

In the meantime Henry was being grilled. (No, don't worry, he hadn't been filleted!)

"We know you didn't come alone. Where is your partner?"

"I already told you I didn't come alone! Why do you keep asking that?"

"That's right, Marie. We've already asked him and he told us. What more do you want?"

"I want details," answered Marie. "Why are you here?"

"I told you, I was helping to set a monument back there at the cemetery. You know? There is a cemetery at the end of your driveway!"

"Don't be a smart ass! I got this knife pointed at your balls and I *will* cut them off!"

"Okay, okay! What else do you want me to tell you? I've already told you that I was setting a monument and I had to pee and I walked back in the woods so nobody could see me."

"You had to walk six hundred feet into the woods so nobody could see you? I don't really think it's that much of a monster," Marie said while looking at Henry's crotch.

"Well, I'm shy."

"Why didn't you go over on the other side of the road?"

"I thought I saw a snake."

"You thought you saw a snake in all that pine straw, but you didn't see any of those 'no trespassing—subject to the extreme castration' signs!"

"Oh! Is that what those were? I wondered why anybody would have a picture of a willy with an X drawn over it."

It was becoming apparent to the ladies that Henry was an idiot. Marie walked over to an old rustic table and thrust the knife down into it, causing Henry to jump.

She called the other girls over to huddle. They were in conference for several minutes, which just sounded like a low rumble to Henry. He craned his neck to try to hear, but the best he could do was to hear one of the girls say, "But I like him . . ." A few seconds later she came over and started fondling his breasts.

Henry began to beam with a little bit of that idiotic Alabama redneck pride. He honestly believed that his simpleton's charm was winning them over. No, it was purely physical.

In the meantime, Craig made it back to the truck, completely out of breath. His "gazellated" gate had slowed to a Galapagos Island tortoise's crawl, but he made it. Exhausted, he barely pulled himself into the truck with the steering wheel and started looking for his clip, which he found after he had thrown everything out onto the ground. He also found Henry's gun when he saw it flying through the air.

He looked at his phone and saw there was no signal at all! He would have to do it alone, but he felt like two fully loaded nine-millimeter pistols evened the odds. He hoped that he would only have to show them, but he was ready to fire off some rounds.

He had an idea! He just hoped that it would work. He backed up to the gate and then used the truck's crane to lift it off its pins. He then turned the truck around and pointed it up the driveway. Instinctively he shut the engine off.

He went to the back of the truck and grabbed a bag of concrete mix and placed it on the hood, which he repeated three more times. He took the tie-down strap and loosely secured the bags.

When he was ready to go, he started up the truck and jammed it into first gear and let out the clutch and killed it!

"Goddam this fucking truck! I swear to God if I win the lottery, I'm buying us a goddam fucking diesel!" he swore as he slammed the steering wheel with his palms a half dozen times.

He started it back up and floored it . . . Killed it! Started it . . . Killed it . . . Started it . . . Killed it . . . Started it . . . Finally! He took off and shifted into second gear while keeping the pedal to the metal. He was revving it so high in second gear on the loose gravel road that the rear end started to come around, but he let up to shift into third, which straightened it out.

He got up to seventy-five miles per hour and covered the quarter mile very quickly. When he got close enough to the front porch of the main house, he slammed on the brakes, flinging the four bags of concrete mix off the hood! It actually worked! It created a huge smoke screen that wafted its way onto the porch.

He jumped out of the truck, leaving it running, and holding his breath, he ran onto the porch and busted the door in. It wasn't locked, but he didn't know that . . . When he and the cloud of dust got into the house, he discovered that the congregants had already moved to another room with Henry. Their yells caught his attention, and when he looked their way, he nearly parted company with his Bojangle's breakfast!

His gag reflex, after seeing all of those naked old lesbians and the naked Henry going to town on them, caused him to fire off a round from each pistol into the floor. Needless to say, this really got their attention!

They all grabbed something to cover their naked bodies, including Henry. Craig thought about shooting him right then and there! But how in the hell would OSHA write up this report?

What about the coroner?

Coroner's Report: naked man shot by coworker at work while having sex with ugly old women. Results—justifiable homicide.

But, didn't happen!

"Henry! What the hell are you doing?" Craig asked coarsely while still holding the pistols on the gang.

"Well, ugh . . . Well, you know . . . I had to pee," Henry answered meekly.

"Dammit Henry! *That's no place to pee!* Now get your fucking clothes and let's get out of here!"

"Yeah, okay . . . Well, ugh . . . Bye girls . . . ugh . . . okay, see ya."

Craig drove very fast out of the driveway, leaving all the stuff that he had thrown out of the truck on the ground, and down the road toward county road 66, then pulled off to make Henry dress.

When the pair got back into Georgia, Craig asked, "What in the hell were you thinking? You could have gotten both of us killed. You're very lucky that I didn't shoot you, because when I saw you with those women . . . Jesus!"

Henry didn't know what to say. He stayed quiet for a little while longer, but by now you know Henry. He started laughing and mumbling while shaking his head

"You know, Craig, I actually think I was turning some of those women. Sometimes it takes a real man, you know!" Henry said with great pride.

"Bull-fucking-shit Henry! Those women saw you as a goddamn lesbian with a goddamn built-in dildo!"

Henry's face sunk. He didn't say another word all of the way back to Hamburg. He barely spoke the rest of the day and went home without saying good-bye.

It wasn't long after that Henry quit. No, it was not the humiliation that did it, even though the ribbing was pretty severe. The fact is that he left his wife and moved in with the lesbians up on Cloud Mountain. Yep, turns out Henry really was a lesbian!

***

On Top of a Mountain Ain't on Top of the World

People who have trouble with reality probably shouldn't be given a dream job. Barry is the perfect example of this statement. He was given autonomy to hire whom he pleased and it pleased him to hire all girls. Most every man at the college figured that Barry was getting lots of sex. He had not had sex in thirteen or fourteen years and was too scared of it to start now.

The work that he gave these girls was so banal it was ridiculous. One of the jobs they would do was ride around in the back of the pickup truck and go to a spot and pick up a single rock and drive all the way back to the other end and put the rock on one of the walls and repeat the process over and over. He also would have them on three separate riding mowers cutting the exact same grass, one behind the other.

He would drive them into town to the Home Depot and pick up three or four two by fours and go back and spend a couple of hours figuring out what they were going to do with them.

They would also get a fifteen-minute break every hour, which meant they would get two fifteen-minute breaks during their three hours of allotted time. Pot and booze were quite often included, creating a very mellow, yet festive work environment. Naturally, this created a certain buzz down on the main campus as well. It also caused quite a bit of jealousy among the student body.

How could the entire college know what was going on except for the administration? If they had had a drug policy in place when they hired Barry a year before they would have never hired him. They actually were suspicious and planted an informant, who was a male, to the work crew. Barry and his girl crew had an inkling of what was going on, particularly since he was something of a paranoid schizophrenic and had no decision in this move.

The informant had absolutely no idea of what he was doing. He had never held a weed trimmer in his life and knew nothing at all about plants. He was perfect for academia but the real world was not his friend. He had the misfortune of being the nephew of one of the administrators as well, but when he was informed of his task, he became prickishly excited.

Barry figured out pretty quickly what was going on and discovered that the guy had no idea what poison ivy looked like. Barry had something of the devil in him so he showed him English ivy and told him that it was poison ivy and conversely showed him poison ivy and told him that it was a particular type of English ivy.

He told him that the 'English' ivy needed to be transplanted to another spot so he showed him the poison ivy and showed him where to replant it. So the guy feigned enthusiasm and eagerly went to work thinking that his faux attitude would alleviate any suspicion.

It was a very warm day and pulling up all of that ivy made the human plant sweat profusely. Even though he was wearing gloves he was not wearing long sleeves, and of course, his arms were coming into constant contact with the poison ivy. The unsuspecting idiot also continuously wiped sweat from his forehead with his forearms.

The next day Barry asked his crew, sans Tim the plant, if anyone knew where Tim was. The girls looked at each other and all shook their heads. Barry had a real good idea where he was, and in fact, Tim was in the school infirmary getting a huge dose of Benadryl. Tim refused to go back to work on the mountain.

The administration later sent one of their more "trusted" workers to the resort, but that didn't work either because this fellow just got stoned with the rest of them and had sex with two of the girls. If Barry had known about the sex, he would have been really pissed (he figured that since he was "above" sex, then everyone else should be too), but he was pleased at the stoning.

The next day the trusted employee informed the school administrators that Barry was doing an excellent job and that there was no need to send any more informants up there, but he himself would check on them from time to time just to be sure. In fact he checked on them every day until Barry caught wind of his actions and basically suspended the girls for a week. This caused all of them to quit without warning. He said he was bored with them and they were all lesbians anyway.

Barry quickly hired four new girls and was very pleased with his choices. Two of the girls he had seen running in their very short shorts and pulled up to them and asked them if they needed a job. They immediately identified Barry as the fun guy up on the mountain and, with boisterous giggles, took the job.

Naturally Barry always had them doing jobs where they had to bend over, but instead of making him horny, it made him depressed. He had confessed to me many times that for him sex was a thief that stole his life force.

Barry obsessed over many of these young women, and when he told me one of them really wanted to go to bed with him, I asked him why didn't he just oblige her and get it over with.

"Because then it's just meaningless sex!" he proclaimed.

"Yeah . . . but sometimes *that's* a helluva lot better than sexless meaning," I mocked.

I knew to say no more when I saw the moribund look on his face. So I changed the subject and started talking about the Braves who had just won another division championship. Changing the subject didn't seem to help him very much, but we did continue with small talk until gradually his mood improved.

After several years Barry had had enough. Living his secluded life led to constant drug use and alcohol abuse. The light had gone out of his eyes, and one morning one of his students, whom strangely enough he had given my phone number, telephoned me in a panic while I was at work.

Barry had locked himself up in the shop building with his truck running. Even though my nerves were like scrambled eggs, I knew that I had to get the girl calmed down.

"I don't know what to do!" she screamed. "Can you come up here? Oh please! You've got to come up here!"

"It will take me too long to get there . . . First thing, Carolyn, find something to bust out a window . . . Then you have to call 911 and let security know what is going on."

"I'll bust out a window, but I can't call 911!"

"But, Carolyn! You have to!"

"I can't! I just can't! I don't want my father to know what's been going on!"

"Don't worry about your father," I said with a calm resolve. "Barry is going to die if you don't do something fast."

It turns out that Carolyn had slept with Barry, not having any idea how fragile he was. To Barry, there was no such thing as meaningless sex.

Next I heard screams and the crashing of glass. Carolyn had taken a friend, and with her help, she got through a window. I then heard her screaming at Barry. He responded painfully slow. She told him that I was on the phone and said that I was coming up there. I could hear that his voice was very hoarse, but he angrily demanded that I not come.

"*NO!* I don't want him to see me like this!"

"But Barry! You need help! You can't be left alone!"

"Then you stay!" he demanded.

"I can't! I've got to go to class. He's coming up here."

"*NO!* I can't let anyone see me like this!"

She returned to me on the phone and said, "Kevin, he said he doesn't want you to come . . . but come anyway . . . I've got to get to class," she finished in a panicky voice and hung up without giving me a chance to respond.

I told everyone at work what was going on and told them that I needed to go out to the college. From the shop to the resort usually took thirty-five to forty minutes, so I had no idea what I was going to find when I got there. On any other day, I would have enjoyed the ride out there immensely. That day was one of the most agonizing days that I had ever had up to that point.

When I finally got to his cabin, I couldn't find him. His truck was there. His dogs were there. The door to his cabin was standing wide open so I went in, expecting to find him dead in his bed. I went out his back door, wondering if he had flung himself from the deck that was a solid twenty feet off the ground. I looked over the railing and did not see him.

I went outside and was about to go wandering through the woods to see if I could find him when a car pulled up with him sitting in the passenger seat. He looked at me with a hang-dog look and apologized with his eyes. I was conflicted between being angry and extremely sad.

I could see him talking to the driver who was one of his student workers. He then got out by himself and she left. Very sheepishly he asked me how I was doing. I was taken aback by this and really didn't know what to say.

"Forget about me, how are you?"

"I'm fine . . . Really, I don't know what all the fuss was about. If I was really trying to kill myself, I would have done it. Carbon monoxide doesn't work . . . I just proved that."

"Barry, you were just lucky that Carolyn came along when she did."

"I wasn't going to die," he said defiantly. "I was just pissed and was trying to scare Carolyn."

"Well, you certainly succeeded in doing that, but still what were you thinking?" I asked him, miffed at his strange attitude.

"Let's not talk about this anymore. Come on, let's go inside. I'm really tired."

Just as we got inside, the phone rang and he begged me to answer. He said that he had a feeling that it was his mother because this was the time of day that she usually called him.

"Barry? Is that you? You don't sound like yourself."

"No, ma'am, it's Kevin."

"Why are you answering the phone? Shouldn't you be at work? Is Barry okay?"

"Oh, yes, ma'am. He's fine. I was just near the phone and he asked me to answer it. He was cleaning up. He's been working on his truck and I was up here to help him. It started smoking really bad and I ran out of the building, but you know how stubborn Barry is. He kept working on it until it quit smoking, but I think he breathed a little bit too much of it," I said, trying to be clever.

"May I talk to him?"

"Sure! He's drying his hands now," I answered and then tried to give Barry the phone, but when I did, he motioned that he just could not talk to her.

"Ma'am, he wondered if he could call you back in a few minutes?"

"You tell him that I'm worried about him and that he *better* call me in a few minutes or I'll get someone to drive me up there."

"Yes, ma'am, I will tell him, and if he doesn't call you, I'll come get you myself. Now don't worry about him. He looks fine."

When I got off the phone with his mother, he told me that he knew she was going to call because she knew what he had just tried to do. He said that she always knew when he was in trouble.

I thought of Polly Roper so I believed him and asked him if he was going to be okay by himself and told him that if he needed me to stay, I could. He assured me that he was okay and that the girl that just dropped him off was coming back with some booze and some pot. Booze and pot were Barry's answer to everything, even hunger on most occasions. I told him that I had to get back to work but, of course, to let me know if he needed me.

When his student returned with the goods, I left and spoke to her on the way to my truck and told her to call me if anything happened. When I got halfway down the mountain I realized how exhausted I was, and when I got back to work, I asked for the rest of the day off. They could all see the look on my face, and on this particular day, they did not argue.

A few days went by and I got an invitation to a cookout at Barry's cabin, so of course I went. I was the third person to arrive and was barely greeted by the two who were already there and who were in a very somber mood. Approximately fifteen more people arrived and every one of them was gripped by a nervous tension.

Contrarily, Barry was in a festive mood. I'm sure everyone that arrived thought that his behavior was extremely odd, but not me. I expected it!

The party started very slowly. The first two who had gotten there before me lit the grill and went inside with all the others. I sat outside on a log by the campfire and had a drink.

Barry came outside with a beer in hand and sat down on an adjacent log and we started talking.

"I couldn't stand it inside," Barry said. "Every damn one of them acts like they're at a funeral. I'm all right, damn it! I told you, if I had really wanted to kill myself, I would have used something besides carbon monoxide."

"Barry, you were just damn lucky! If Carolyn had not come up here when she did, we wouldn't be here talking."

"I'm telling you," he said emphatically, "I'm living proof that carbon monoxide *does not* work! I was already in there an hour before she got here."

"Okay . . . You're probably right," I said panderingly. "Either that or you're extremely tough. I know that if I had been in there an hour, I would definitely be dead."

"Nah . . . You're tougher than I am."

I took a purposeful swig of my drink and spoke of it no more.

***

The real reason that Barry didn't die was because the ventilation system in the shop building was very good and it sucked out most of the exhaust. Maybe Barry turned it on before he started his truck and knew that if his "girlfriend" arrived in time that he would have no problem surviving. I just believe that he was so arrogant he really believed that he was indestructible.

The couple in charge of the steaks came back outside and started cooking. I tried to make small talk with them, but they didn't seem interested. I sat on the log and finished my drink.

"How is it that you know, Barry?" one of them finally asked.

"Oh . . . Well, the truth is that we were cellmates in prison." I couldn't tell you how many times I heard that question and that was always how I answered it and it always made Barry laugh. Of course, Barry did look like someone who had been in prison.

The couple was not amused; they looked really troubled, as though they actually believed what I said. Barry never played along with my little joke and he quickly told them that he worked for me at the monument company.

The couple looked relieved and went back to cooking the steaks and back to ignoring me. That was fine with me; they were boring as hell anyway, so I went inside to see just how boring the rest of the crowd was. They were pretty damn boring too.

Eventually the steaks were served and we all took our places to eat. Barry was sitting next to me at a table with four other people. Some were in the living room and some were at two other tables in the same dining room as us.

Absolutely no one was talking. People looked more like they were playing with their food. Barry and I were eating heartily, but still not talking. I couldn't stand the pins and needles, so I spoke up.

"You know . . . This is the *best damn post suicide party* I have *ever* been to."

Barry busted out laughing so hard that food came out of his mouth! Then he said that I was awesome. Most of the rest of them looked aghast, but then a few of the others joined in with laughter. The ice was broken and the evening became a real party.

Bobby and the Confederate Gold

"Hey, Clem, where's the gold?"
        "Hell, Flem, I thought you got it!"

I was just slightly two months removed from my fortieth birthday and was feeling the pangs of perceived middle age. I felt like that I had peaked at nineteen months old when I climbed that pole and had done nothing close to what my late grandfather had done. At this particular point, I didn't have a whole lot of anything to brag about.

I was chomping at the bit for something to get on about, to participate in some kind of high-risk, possible-reward endeavor. I started having dreams about mountains of treasure and would always wake up after I discovered that what I had found in the dream was only chocolate candy covered in gold-colored tinfoil.

There were times when I would get up in the middle of the night, trying not to disturb my wife, and go to the kitchen and dig out a piece of chocolate candy and look at it pensively by the soft glow of the little night lamp that was plugged in at the back of the counter. Sometimes I would put it back, seeing that it might be two o'clock in the morning, but most nights I'd eat it.

I'd go back to bed, not having brushed my teeth, and when I would awaken to the alarm clock, that chocolate that still resided in my mouth would give me morning breath that would knock shit off a buzzard wagon. You know what I mean.

For some reason, I started thinking about Bobby and all the crazy stuff we did—mostly that he did. I wondered how he was getting along and if he had ever settled down or if he was still crazy as hell.

Timing is everything, yet I thought that a phone call that I got from Bobby, out of nowhere, was still just a coincidence. A self-appointed sage once told me that there are no coincidences. I feel like I could probably confirm that statement.

I had not seen Bobby in twenty years or so, which was why I told myself that I was surprised by his phone call, but really wasn't. I went off into some sort of weird trance for a moment and believed he said, but wouldn't swear to it, "Hey, Kavin, how is everything . . ."

Kavin was what he called me growing up, which was what snapped me out of that trance very quickly. In order to tolerate this indignation that always drove my mother and me nuts, I concentrated on the nostalgia of better things.

"Fine, Bobby, how's everything with you?"

"I haven't seen you in a long time, so I thought we should get together . . . You know just to talk about old times."

I had no idea that whirling dervishes could be sentimental, but I figured, what would be the harm? After exchanging pleasantries and updates, we decided to meet at one of the old gang's favorite pizza parlors.

When we met at the restaurant, we shook hands, exchanged slaps on the back and bodacious grins, but I couldn't help noticing the look of brevity in his eyes.

After ordering our pizza, we took up the conversation we had started on the phone but Bobby quickly transitioned into a more businesslike tone.

"Kavin, I was wondering if you knew much about the mausoleums in Rose Hill?"

"I do . . . Bobby? Why do you always call me Kavin?"

"Well, it's your name, isn't it?"

"It's Kevin! Ev, not av!"

"It is? Well . . . dadgum . . . *Kevin*, how much *do* you know?"

"What do you mean? What do you want to know?"

"I want to know if you have heard anything out of the ordinary about any of them."

I was dumbfounded by this question, mainly due to the coincidence of the timing and was already figuring him out. I looked around to see if anyone was listening but noticed no one. Still, I lowered my voice and described a scene that I had witnessed not long before.

"Funny you should ask. This is kind of weird, well any way, we got a phone call . . . about a month ago . . . from one of the funeral homes asking if we could meet a couple of their men over at Rose Hill at the big Warren mausoleum." I paused to sip some water.

"When we got there, we saw a casket lying on the floor . . . Some vandals had broken into two of the crypts . . . one above the other . . . and dragged the lower casket out onto the floor . . . It was an old cast-iron deal . . . The lid was busted open and you could see a skeleton. Some of the cloth from his suit was still there, but it looked like, if you tried to pick it up, it would just crumble to nothing. Anyway, what they wanted us for was to remove the crypt fronts so they could get all the other bodies out and move them to another cemetery."

"Really! Why'd they want to do that?"

"Well, because that was like the fourth or fifth time that this particular mausoleum was vandalized. They were tired of worrying. On top of that, every other mausoleum over there seems to be broken into once or twice a year."

"Was there a casket in the upper one?" Bobby asked.

"Yeah . . . yeah, but the vandals didn't get that one out because it was a wooden one. See, the handle on the end pulled right off . . . I mean, the casket was rotten."

"Did it stink in there?"

"I'm glad to see that you're still Bobby! But, anyhow, what makes you ask a crazy question like that?"

"I was just curious, that's all."

"Still seems strange, but anyway . . . It was kinda musty, but the dead people smell was almost gone . . . Well, it didn't stink . . . until they pulled a baby's casket out of one of the fronts that we moved."

"Why did that one stink?"

"Well, because, when they pulled it out, about half way, the whole end pulled loose, and this liquid, along with the head, rolled right out onto the floor! Ugh! It was gross."

Bobby seemed totally unaffected by this detail and asked, "Were you able to see back behind any of the crypts?"

"Oh yeah! I didn't mention that the Warren mausoleum was built back into the hillside. You know, most of them are freestanding, except for another one that's right below. Normally, the outer walls are four to six inches thick, but since the Warren's back wall was the hill, they just put a two-inch piece of marble at the back of the crypts. So behind the crypt, where the vandals had broken into, they also broke through that thin wall. So you could see that it looked like a narrow cave."

That was the word Bobby was waiting for—"cave."

"Could you see how deep it was?" he asked, barely able to stay in his seat.

"You couldn't tell how far back it was, because it had been bricked in about ten feet back. They were old bricks too. I bet they dated back to before the civil war."

"They might have, but it's possible that hole wasn't plugged up until much later. Do you know when the mausoleum was built?"

"It says '1882' above the entrance."

Bobby sat back and began to drum the table with his fingers. I'd never seen him in a thoughtful repose, and I was glad to see that he could sit still, but there was something disturbing about his demeanor.

"It's good that that wall was still intact. It means that we still have time," he said most seriously.

"Who has time and for what?"

"You and I, for one, and something worth way more than its face value, for what," he said with a twist of the devil in his eye.

"It's the Confederate gold, isn't it? I knew it!" I said, looking off into the distance.

"I didn't say anything about gold. Confederate or otherwise."

"Well, I would think that if it was Confederate money, then the paper would have rotted in that hill, as damp as it is."

"How in Sam Hill did you know it had to do with anything Confederate, let alone the Confederate gold?"

"Because when I told a friend of my brother who's a Civil War buff about the vandalism and what looked like a cave, he said 'hmm, might be the Confederate gold in there,' and there have been three or four other dudes that have said pretty much the same thing. He said that the gold had never been found. Then he asked me if we could get in there again without anybody from the city knowing about it."

"What did you tell him?"

"I told him no because, by the time we finished putting the crypt fronts back on, there was already a crew there waiting to bar up the entrance, along with putting a heavy chain and padlock through the opening of the bronze doors."

"If other people believe the gold might be in there, we may not have as much time as I thought."

I thought Bobby was being a little overdramatic, but then again it *was* Bobby.

The pizza came and Bobby ate his half in the style of his youth, with one breath and whirling elbows and a total disregard for whether it all made it into his mouth. I still haven't finished mine, for which I would have been pissed except I remembered the story of how my grandfather's fortunes changed on the night that he didn't get to finish his supper, and happily I was beginning to feel his presence.

"Bobby?" I asked when we got outside of the restaurant.

"Yeah?"

"How did you come to the conclusion that there might be the Confederate gold in Rose Hill?"

"I came across an accident and this old guy had a really old map clutched in his dying hands. As he was gasping his last breaths, he whispered, 'Gold, the confederate gold . . . You must get to it before the Yankees get it,' And then . . . aaarg . . . he died."

As incredible as it seemed, no. It *was* bullshit.

"How?" I asked sardonically.

"When I was a kid, my grandfather told me that his father was an errand boy for the Confederates while they were holed up in Rose Hill . . . You know it was a fort before they made it a cemetery?"

"Yeah, I knew it was a fort in the civil war, but it was a cemetery first."

"It was? Are you sure?"

"Yep. There's a plaque on the front entrance . . . 1850 something."

Looked like he doubted me, but my look told him to quit it. That's how I handled him when we were kids. He would mock words, but that look I gave him was sometimes followed with a fist to his arm, which was rather more difficult to mock.

"All right then. My great-grandfather said one of the officers told him that that cave was the ammo dump, and if that powder went up, then Hamburg was going to be showered with gold. Then he showed him a gold coin that he said he snuck out of a tin box."

"That still doesn't prove that there is gold in that cave. I mean, they probably got it out. If they left it, the Yanks could have found it."

We walked on out to our cars and continued our conversation away from the other patrons who were beginning to arrive in large numbers.

"The whole point is, is that the gold disappeared and nobody knows where. And an addendum to that point is that the Confederates were not as brilliant and efficient as we like to believe. So I believe that when they pulled out . . . you know the Yankees were braced for a hellacious fight here, but Joe Johnston pulled out thousands of troops, horses, and wagons—everything—and the Yankees never even heard them leave. Anyway, when the Rebs pulled out, I believe, and so do a few others, that they forgot to assign a detail to pull out the gold."

"But how could they just forget it?"

"I have to think that when they were given the order to skedad-dle, the soldiers had no idea there was any gold mixed in with the ammo, so once they got all of what they thought was in there out, they got the hell out of there themselves . . . without the gold."

"I don't know, Bobby . . . If it was left in there, I believe it would have been on purpose. I mean, you know of at least one officer who knew it was there and I'll just bet that he found a hiding place."

We talked as though we knew his great-grandfather's story to be the absolute truth and not a legend. I suppose that if we had believed it to be only a legend, then we would not have committed so per-functorily to such a harebrained endeavor.

We were about to find out one way or another. We had chosen eight thirty Christmas Eve night. We hoped that everyone in town was where we wanted them to be, at parties or scurrying to and fro to ready their homes for Santa and the too-short night that follows. It seemed logical to us that they would be anticipating the joyful holiday with friends and family and not giving a rat's ass what two weirdoes were doing slinking around a mausoleum.

That's what I was thinking along with how the illegality of our impending action was making me nervous. The worst things that I had ever done were sneak extra cookies and drink my mother's wine, refilling with water what I had drunk. Well, I did look up a girl's dress once . . . and I stole a piece of gum—okay! I'm a sinner. I might as well make it count!

The cemetery rises near the confluence of the Donwannadoit and Wachamacallit Rivers, which forms the Emtipoo River, which also formed the center of downtown Hamburg. At the top stands a ten-foot-tall granite confederate that faces north, holding his granite musket as though his stare might still save the town from hordes of Yankee invaders.

I told Bobby that that was a good sign because that sucker wouldn't see us coming to steal his gold, since we would be approaching from the east.

He gave me a dirty look as though I was serious. He himself had always had a sophomoric sense of humor, so it burned my butt that he didn't at least smile at my joke.

We parked our trucks at the park that was situated on the other side of the river from the cemetery. It sat behind a levee that was built to protect the town from floods. There was no need of a levee on the cemetery side for a quarter mile because most of the ground there was a good deal higher.

The park was where the gays "hung out" and the cops ignored them, so I felt marginally sure that they would ignore us too.

We were both wearing long coats to conceal our tools. Bobby brought metal cutting tools, a hammer, and other sundry items.

Among other things, I brought a couple of ropes that I had the bright idea to loop and hang them around each shoulder under my coat. Even though the coat was two sizes too large, it did not adequately conceal the ropes, making my head almost disappear, so I perched my hat as high up on my head as I could and hoped the wind wouldn't blow. If I didn't arouse suspicion after that, then it was proof that no one was paying attention.

We crossed the river junction over an old railroad bridge and walked another four hundred yards on the opposite side of the river from the cemetery until we came to the South Main Street bridge and turned right toward the cemetery.

When I looked up at the dilapidated old cemetery, its terraces reminded me of a wedding cake that had been plopped down too hard, causing its tiers to sag to the point that one more jolt would cause them to slide off into the river; the granite soldier, the groom, seemed to be looking for his bride that must have already been jarred from her perch into the river.

I never noticed how bad it had looked before, but I had never seen it from this perspective. The sparse streetlights below cast shadows at an upward slant that gave it a sinister air.

I was beginning to have grave doubts. Hmmmm. The mausoleum and the entire terrace we were about to molest were hidden perfectly by the shadows.

We were not pros, but we thought that we thought of every scenario that we could to prevent mistakes. The main thing that we discussed was to stay loose. I thought that Bobby would actually have a harder time staying focused because of the way he was as a child, but I had nearly forgotten that the entire time he was in school he never missed one single math problem. Not one! So my anxieties eased a little knowing that when his mind was made up, his emotions were dead—period.

I was one of those naysayers who could think of a million problems and two million reasons why we shouldn't attempt this endeavor and I kept telling him that we needed a little more preparation, while Bobby was one of the few who could think of the one solution and the one reason why we should and that we didn't want to overthink this thing. In effect this made us a perfect team.

I tried to engage in light conversation, but Bobby kept quiet and a keen eye out for danger. All the while he studied with voracity the terrain, to see if anything had changed from our dozen walkthroughs.

Since I couldn't turn my head, lest my hat fell off, I just kept walking like a zombie returning to its grave, until we turned off South Main toward the main entrance. As soon as we got to within twenty-five or thirty feet of the main entrance, which was on the opposite side of the hill from the mausoleum, we ducked behind a huge magnolia that had been left unpruned. Its waxy leaves reached the ground and provided us with a tremendous shadow.

We weaved our way through the old stones, staying within the shadows whenever it provided our best cover, stumbling more than once on invisible footstones, climbing banks from one terrace to another, sometimes taking two steps forward and slipping one step backward on the dew-covered grass.

When we got to within a few yards of our goal, we both froze in our tracks due to the unwelcomed sounds of heavy breathing and obviously some really hard-core diddly doodling coming from the top of the mausoleum!

"Fuck!" was all I said, probably a little louder than what I should have.

The sounds from above stopped. Bobby took out his club of a flashlight and climbed partway up the bank and shined it toward the horny couple and shouted, "You motherfucker! What in hell are you doing with my wife?"

Bobby was off the mark just a wee bit. Well, you see because . . . It was two dudes! But never-the-less they didn't argue with this minor misrepresentation of the facts. Their ensuing actions, however, did seem to argue with the fact that it was a little chilly and that britches are somewhat handy toward combatting this little unpleasantry.

Bobby kept the light on their faces to keep them from seeing us. They grabbed their blankets and took off as fast as they could, with their shiny white behinds bobbing along with mercurial alacrity in the incandescent beam until they were out of sight.

My heart was pounding out of my chest, so much so that I thought I saw a flashing red light but realized that what I was seeing were my very own veins pulsating in my very own eyeballs!

As soon as I regained my composure, I yelled at a whisper, which caused my voice to crack, "Bobby turn off that damn light!" then I started to cough and wheeze.

Bobby turned toward me, shining the light under his own chin, making a ghoulish howl, then he started to laugh his scare-the-shit-out-of-a-banshee laugh.

"Look! Bobby! Get a grip on yourself!"

A couple of more huck-ucks and phewwws, bending at the waist with his hands on his knees, he looked up at me and said, "I bet those motherfuckers were a little confused as to which one of 'em was my wife!" and a more human laughter began to rain down.

I tried to restrain my laughter, but it came out like a bucket of water knocked off a ledge.

"I think they ran off without their pants," Bobby said. "Let's go see if they're up there." He motioned toward the top of the mausoleum.

Sure enough they had left their pants along with their wallets and car keys. This fact sobered us very quickly, especially when I found out who they were. I pulled out my tiny penlight and shone it on the ID. "Well, motherfucker! Bobby, one of those gentlemen is our sheriff!" I said after checking out his wallet. "And I bet these are the keys to his sheriff's car!"

Bobby checked the other wallet and asked, "Who is G. Gardner Alexander?"

"That is our esteemed juvenile court judge . . . Holy shit!"

"All right," he said coolly, "we're going to have to leave this stuff here and walk back down to broad street as deliberately and calmly as we can so that we don't attract any more attention."

"I agree, but I don't think we should wear our coats back down. I have the key to that mausoleum down there," I said, pointing to the terrace below.

He quickly caught on to what I was getting at and suggested that we hurry, which we did, and with that he yelled loud enough that households from three blocks over could hear, "Hey, you motherfuckers! We're leaving now and you can come get your pants!"

Unable to see any steps I told Bobby to make haste. (I like that term "to make haste." Don't you? "Friend, why are you in such a hurry?" "Why, I'm making haste of course!") We would have to slide down the bank to the drive below. I went first, and as I was sliding down, my foot caught a tree root, which flipped me head over heels! Since I had the two coils of rope wrapped around each shoulder, they cushioned my descent somewhat, but at the same time made it difficult for me to regain my control.

For some idiotic reason I had pulled my legs into the fetal position, which accelerated my decline! I was beginning to worry that I was going to keep on rolling right into the river, but just when I was about to go over the next and steepest bank, I straightened out my legs and practically did a head stand, which I had never been able to do on purpose, and came crashing down on my back!

The stubborn thing that I am, I rolled over and stood up as fast as I could to prove that I wasn't injured. The silly thing though is that I found myself quite drunk, which very nearly caused me to stagger my way right off the rest of that damn cemetery.

The ground, however, promptly came to my aid by flying up to me and kissing my face. What passion! It haunted me for days after. Again, fortunately, the ropes cushioned the blow so that I was still basically unharmed, though a little bruised. It . . . it could have been worse.

I was fixing to get up one more time when Bobby said as quietly as he could, "Kavin, stay the hell down until you can stand the hell up."

I admit that his logic would have been a bit thorny to oppose so I readily conformed to his very sympathetic suggestion. As soon as the earth quit spinning in the wrong direction, I stood up with the feeling that my face was warped, with my left eye and ear two inches above my right. Of course, it was the glasses.

Bobby was already down the bank and standing in front of me before I regained my senses. Apparently, I stood there staring blankly at him with a goofy grin.

"Kavin!" He gave me a shake.

"Damn it, Bobby! Why do you have to call me Kavin?"

"Kavin!"

"Seriously, Bobby—"

"Damn it, Kavin, snap out of it. I see a cop car leaving the station over there!"

And he could. Three blocks away on the western side of the Wachamacallit was the police station and I saw him too.

Snap out of it, I did. I pulled out the key, which had miraculously stayed in my pocket, and with a little effort I . . . tried . . . grunted . . . groaned . . . Key won't turn . . . seems to be bending . . . I think it's going to break . . . Oops, wrong key . . . Cop's getting closer . . . Where is that other key . . . Cop's turning down street . . . Did it fall out? . . . Cop's unlocking main gate . . . Shu wee! Here it is, tangled up in this damn tissue I used to blow my nose . . . Cop's getting back into car . . . Wrong key won't come out . . . Cop's proceeding slowly up main drive . . . Bobby takes out pliers . . . pulls "wrong key" out . . . Cop turns left at top of hill . . . We unlock door . . . Cop checks cemetery office, gets back into car . . . We try to enter mausoleum at same time, making tools clang . . . Cop turns car toward top of hill . . . Can't see cop but know he's heading toward Confederate statue . . . take off heavy coats, lay them in corners away from door . . . Cop drives around statue shining car's spotlight . . . We get out of mausoleum . . . lock it back . . . Cop stops car . . . Cop gets out . . . We sneak away . . . Cop checks Warren mausoleum . . . Cop finds pants . . . We head back up hill behind wall . . . We hear cop car still running . . . Cop finds steps to drive below . . . cop takes steps . . . We take car . . . Cop doesn't know at first . . . Cop must be spooked . . . We ease downhill . . . Cop has light bulb go off in head . . . We head toward main gate . . . Cop sees car leaving cemetery . . . Cop starts waving . . . We wave back . . . We duck down . . . head toward rough part of town . . . I look back . . . see cop running . . . Cop falls down . . . We drive down back streets . . . spotlight blazing . . . Don't know how to turn it off . . . Kids probably think Santa checking to see if they're in bed.

I directed Bobby through several turns to get us to an old cemetery that was overgrown with blackberries and privet. I figured that we could ditch the car there and make our way back to Rose Hill. Even though I had never taken the trail to the river, I figured to take it this time so that no one could see which direction we took.

"There's a cemetery right around this next curve. You'll barely be able to see it because of all the brush," I assured him. "There's a place to pull in right in the middle."

Ugh-oh.

"Shit damn fuck! Goddam mother fucking son of a bitch!" I said.

There was no brush! It was *clean*! On top of that, some of the neighbors had a nice little campfire going with about ten to fifteen potential witnesses in a rather celebratory kind of attitude.

"To hell with it! Pull in there anyway. Head all the way to the back."

At the back of the cemetery was a huge, concrete bible with its immense pages turned to the Ten Commandments. I did not appreciate the Lord's obvious sense of humor because when we stopped, the headlights shone, with the utmost peculiar precision, on "THOU SHALT NOT STEAL."

Bobby angled the car so that the spotlight would blind the pious revelers, which instantly turned them into pissed revelers. Oh, the profanity! Mine was tame. Pissed profanity has a much different nuance than scared profanity!

My side of the car was on the opposite side from all the joyful noise, which was a good thing. I got out as fast as I could, but I still got bowled over by a very pumped up Tasmanian Devil who came out on my side also.

My clothes were beginning to get a little soggy by now from all the rolling around I had done, but I knew that if I was going to save my ass, I was going to have to make the rest of me drag it on to the riverbank and hightail it back to Rose Hill!

I had not known until that night that there was a levee behind the Ten Commandments. This was the best news so far because once we headed over it, we could go in any direction we wanted. Except home. That was sure 'nuff where I wanted to be.

To Rose Hill, we flew like the wind . . . Sort of. You have to stay up on the grassy areas of a riverbank or when the silty part is wet, which it was—swoosh! You're in the river . . . nasty, foul-smelling putrescence . . . And people fish that river!

Slinking along in a Groucho Marx sort of trot, we could hear the sirens of four or five cop cars coming from all directions. We were closing in on Rose Hill when we came to a gully that was a little too wide to negotiate, so we headed back up the bank. We had gotten about forty yards up and into someone's backyard when we heard that damned ol' heavy breathing again coming from the opposite side of where we had just been.

They weren't "messing around" though. They were just out of breath from trying to get away from being seen. It would've worked for them if it hadn't been for Bobby and me. Wouldn't you know it, sitting right next door to where we had come up from the river sat our esteemed sheriff's official government-issued sheriff car, where an obvious party was going on and to where both of our esteemed public officials were trying to get to. I don't know, maybe one of them had a couple of extra pairs of pants hidden somewhere.

I had always hated Bobby's heinous laugh . . . Until now. You see, when he saw those two lovers laboriously plodding, out of breath, up from the river toward the car, his laugh burst out like the flames from a giant furnace with more ferocity than I had ever heard.

The sheriff, who was leading the way, rigidified with such tautness that the judge, who was not light on his feet, bumped into him and lost his footing. I would have told him to stay off the silty part, but nobody ever listens to me . . . But still, he was just a little bit on the silty part, which is akin to the slightly liquid discharges of a little baby.

Yes! Swoosh, he did . . . right into the river! That roiling tumultuous junction of the river . . . Swoosh! There went the sheriff!

"I wonder," asked Bobby matter of factly, "just how many people he's sent up the river?"

"Yeah, but he's going down the river!"

I started to laugh (somebody once told me that I'd laugh in the face of the devil; he was being proven right, just about now!) but I had to stifle it quickly when suddenly, several porch lights came on so we decided to slink on out of there. Fortunately there was a lot of yelling coming from the river, so the good folks of the neighborhood looked in the opposite direction from Bobby and me.

As we got to the outer perimeter of Rose Hill, I looked across the river at my truck and felt that I might as well be looking at the moon.

We crossed the street to get back to the cemetery, and as we entered the luminescence of a streetlight, I looked at my watch and thought that it must have stopped. Unbelievably it showed 9:07. It had not stopped! Thirty seven minutes had stretched to eternity. That's the funny thing about time; have fun and it flies. Can you tell? We weren't having fun.

We decided that we would ease our way back to the lower mausoleum, which belonged to the Morgans. Our company had been entrusted with keys to several mausoleums in order to expedite the removal of crypt doors for future entombments, which is why I was in possession of this particular key.

The reason I had brought the Morgan key was because it and the Warren key looked very similar, and due to the fact that they were in the back of a desk drawer with no tags, I couldn't tell which was which.

From the road, we could see the blue light coming from the top of the hill. Bobby started up the first of four very long flights of steps that led up to the rear of the office. I figured that whatever he did, his bread always seemed to land buttered side up, so I followed him, even though personally I would have gone on a little farther before heading up.

After we negotiated the ninety-six steps that ended at the basement of the office, we turned left and followed the terrace on around to some steps that led up to the drive where the Morgan mausoleum was.

There was a set of steps directly across the drive from where we came up, which Bobby decided to ascend so that he might get closer to the police car in order to possibly hear or see what was going on. I went on to the mausoleum to prepare to get our stuff out as soon as the coast was clear and to rest from all of those damn steps. I knew that if I went with him, my exhausted lungs would give us away and was worried that they might, two levels down from the cops, anyway.

I unlocked the chain and leaned against the stones of the entrance, gazing at the world that I felt that I had just left behind.

The blue lights were dancing about the trees like Tinker Bell in heat when suddenly they moved away and bounded from house to house, flashing down the street that Bobby and I had taken fifteen minutes earlier.

Bobby came down the steps toward me as cool as a cucumber and said, "The coast is clear. They think the two guys in the river took the cop car. There was a sergeant who picked up the patrolman at the top of the hill. They got a call that one of the men was yelling that he was the sheriff, which is when they took off."

At that moment the red lights of two ambulances and a rescue vehicle began to dance around, the sirens following shortly after.

I was really proud of the response time of all our public servants, but at the same time, I wished that they were not so damned efficient.

I was hoping too that they would get those two lovers out of that frigid water alive, and that I could go about my business and go into denial, just like most people do.

"Bobby, let's get our stuff and get out of here. If we get down there to the bridge without being seen, I'll throw the rope underneath. I don't think my other stuff will attract any attention . . . Shit, where's my hat?" I said as I felt of my head.

"What are you talking about?"

"My hat! It fell off . . . God knows where!" I said with my eyes motoring back and forth as though I was searching for it in my mind.

"No, Kavin, why are you talking about leaving before we give this thing a shot?"

Even with all the difficulties we were having, I was still more pissed off with him calling me Kavin than anything else.

I inhaled deeply to calm down and said, "I think somebody is trying to tell us something. I don't want to break into that mausoleum after all this crap and discover there is no gold, and besides even if there is, I don't think I want it!"

"Oh come on! We find that gold and everything'll look different."

"Yeah! And when they find my hat, they'll come to our office and I'll buckle under the first question: 'what's your name?' 'I did it! I killed the sheriff! It was me!' And things will look different behind bars!"

You see, I thought that I had worn my Hamburg Monument Co. hat. I was seeing the worst-case scenario, that they had already found it and that when they questioned the sheriff, if he was still alive, he would say that he saw us, and that I was wearing a hat.

"Yeah, and when we find the gold, you can hire the best damn attorney there is or you can buy the judge. Besides, other than being in a cemetery after dark, what will they get you for?"

So we got our stuff from the Morgan Mausoleum so that we could return to the scene of the impending crime. I was in the entrance looking out at Bobby as we talked. I felt that I was really looking for an escape when I thought that I saw my hat in a tree that was growing in the bank below.

"I think there's my hat!"

He turned to look and picked up a stick and knocked it out on the first try, where it fell a few feet down the slope. Before I could step around him to retrieve it, he held his hand against my chest and said, "I'll get it." He got it and returned it to me. It was my hat all right, but it didn't say Hamburg Monument Co. It said "G," for Georgia Bulldogs.

"Oh well . . . I forgot."

"See! Damn it, Kavin, you're starting to sound like Jack! If you want something, you go for it!"

He was right of course. I was one of those people who always wanted to want. If I got it, then I couldn't want it. It was at that moment that I remembered climbing that poll to touch the ceiling. Now it appeared that I was going to touch that ceiling one more time. So I removed one of the wants and replaced it with, "To hell with mediocrity and to hell we go. Let's kick those Yankee bastards in the nuts and win this war!"

Bobby was quite amused, but to his credit, he restrained his laugh, which caused snot to explode from his nose (probably the mold; we got lots of it). He wiped it with his sleeve and put on his coat, which was my cue that the party was still on.

There we were standing in front of the Warren mausoleum. Any feeling that I might have had was gone. A true sense of purpose had taken over. I had convinced myself that what we were doing was a rescue mission, unless of course there was no gold.

Regardless of anything else, the first order of business was to get in. The iron gate had been placed inside the opening in front of the bronze doors with three bolts on each side screwed into lead anchors sunken into the limestone with the heads welded to the gate. There was enough space between the gate and the stone to get a cutting tool into position to slice the bolts.

Bobby pulled out a small battery-powered die grinder, but before he could start cutting, I stopped him.

"Look, Bobby, if you start cutting with that grinder, the sparks are going to light up this mausoleum like the Fourth of July."

Without a word, he put it back in his coat and pulled out a mini battery-powered reciprocating saw and grinned. I, being the one without a degree in anything, would have just brought a small hand-operated hacksaw, but what can I say?

The metal workers had only used soft number two grade bolts, which the saw compromised with ease. If they had used case hardened steel, then the grinder would have been our only choice.

We had decided early on that, if we could, we would only cut one side so that all we would have to do was pull the gate open far enough to get in and pull it back once we were inside.

It worked. Having been afforded the luxury of the gate as leverage the soft bolts bent easily. I then opened the padlock and realized that the bronze doors opened outwardly, so we could only open one door, but it was wide enough to get in with a little gut sucking and breath holding. Ten years and twenty pounds later, I would've never made it.

We took the chain that held the padlock and wrapped it once around the second bar so that we could pull the gate to through the window of the door. We had to pull it as far as we could to start with so that the chain would reach.

Once that feat was accomplished, Bobby pulled out an opaque black curtain and draped it over the entire door to prevent our lights from being seen.

We each pulled out our homemade miner's lights that we had made from headbands and those little flat multi-directional flash-lights and put them on in unison. We tried to give each other that knowing look, but we temporarily blinded each other due to the direct aim of our lights.

Even without being able to see, I pulled out my T-handles that are made for removing crypt fronts and took off my coat and threw down the ropes. These particular fronts were supplied with little rosettes on each side. T-handles are screwed into the centers of the rosettes so the front can be removed. On each end of the crypt open-ing, there are grooves that the front is placed in. They are removed by pulling it to one side to pull out one end and sliding it back to get the other end out.

Usually the fronts are sealed, which would slow our efforts enormously, but now absent of bodies, there was no need for them to have been sealed, so our crypt front of choice came out easily.

I warned Bobby that the front was heavier than it looked, but he still let his end drop down with a solid clank, knocking off a cor-ner, causing me to cringe.

I reminded myself that it really didn't matter, since it was one of the doors that we had pieced back together anyway and no descen-dants were ever going to come back to make a fuss. After I got over my unwarranted analocity, I noticed the musty air emanating from the cave.

After setting down the door, I crawled through the crypt and into the larger opening. With my light beaming, I stood up to look around and was surprised to see how dry it actually was.

Bobby came in behind me, still wearing his coat, and headed toward the bricks that I had told him about and placed his hands on them as though he wanted to caress them.

He took out a medium-sized punch and three-pound drilling hammer and began to hammer out the aged mortar as quietly as he could. The mortar was very soft, which actually caused it to resist his attempt.

After a good five minutes he still had not gotten out the first brick.

"Bobby, if you'll just drive the punch in with the hammer and then dig it out [meaning the mortar], it'll come out a lot quicker."

"I'm doing this!" he said pissed-offedly.

"Oh! I forgot . . . You're an engineer . . . Common sense don't mean shit compared to a Phd!"

He handed me the hammer and punch and stepped back, folding his arms and tapping his foot with notable irritation.

"See?" I said as I took out the first brick.

It became obvious that there was another layer behind the first one.

"CRAP!" I exclaimed.

Bobby began to exclaimate too, but in fact we had earlier discussed the probability that the wall would be double bricked. We were simply a little fragged out by our previous unforeseen exertion so that our hope exceeded our expectation.

In our excitement to get in as quickly as we could, we had forgotten to bring in a candle that we had deemed important to check the oxygen in the cave, considering that it had been obstructed from any fresh air for most of the last hundred and ten years, but it's pretty obvious that the front door was letting in plenty of air. Amateurs are more likely to think of useless things like candles, I suppose.

Bobby went back into the foyer and retrieved my coat and handed it to me to take out the candle and a book of matches. The matches were slightly damp from all of my rolling around. Owing to that fact, they were reluctant to light.

After fifteen attempts I took out three matches and folded the flap over the striking surface, with the matches in between, and gave them a quick pull. This time they lit and I did the same to the candle. I placed the candle on the floor next to my right and started to go back to work, but as I turned, I did a double-take, noticing that the flame was leaning toward me. I moved slowly away to see if it was some sort of attraction thing, but it kept leaning to its left with a lively flicker.

Bobby and I said in unison, "There's air coming from somewhere!" And it wasn't coming from the front of the mausoleum.

We looked to the right and saw a small very dark hole in the cave wall. We went over to it, and as we began to examine it, part of it fell loosely to our feet.

At the same time, the two of us took our hands and gave a stout push to the edge of the hole and I was surprised at least that the wall crumbled and I went in head first! Eerily I had a flashback to the sawdust pile, but this time there was no Jack. Bobby escaped the falling earth, I suspected because he had enough sense not to push so hard. I also suspected that his engineering background finally overcame his nature and made him a little more cautious.

I was stuck, barely escaping being struck by a sizable stone. Bobby, still on the other side, quickly spoke to make sure that I was okay. I assured him that I would live, provided that he didn't wait too long to get me out. (At that moment I remembered my grandfather being stuck for what must have felt like eternity to him, which made me feel exceedingly ashamed.) I did have one arm relatively free so I started to dig my way out.

Bobby climbed over the rubble to get to my face, which his body weight briefly made it even more difficult to breathe. When he got over, what I heard him say was, "Holy mother of God!"

I wondered if blood was pouring out of my head or something, but I barely got my head turned enough to see what he was Holy-Mother-of-Godding about.

There was, I guess you could say, a sentinel made mostly of bones that must have been left there to die. He was still holding a very rusty bayoneted musket. He was still in his uniform, sort of, and his hat was still on his head. He looked Confederate all right.

Bobby turned to dig me out, which only took a minute or two, and said, "Well, I'd say we're on the right track."

My asthma was starting to get the better of me so I didn't reply right away. Bobby looked at me and told me to rest a minute. I retrieved my flashlight from the rubble and shined it around to look for a suitable place to sit. I noticed a dirt ledge so I went to sit down.

"There is no way!" I shouted.

"What!"

I shined my light toward the sentinal. The words "Gone but not for fartin'" were inscribed above his head in the cave wall.

"There is no fucking way! Ron Anderson used to say that all the time when he lettered stones. Could it be possible that he'd been in here?"

"If he had he still might not have found the gold, so come on and let's start looking."

If Ron had been in there and found the gold, he didn't live like it. Dad said that he died poor, mainly due to consuming way too much alcohol. But still . . .

I got up to examine the lettering, and as I walked across the small cavern, my steps began to make a metallic clink. Of course Bobby and I immediately went to the floor on all fours. What we found were around thirty gold and silver coins. We were somewhat disappointed that most of them appeared to have been minted in Mexico . . . Mexico?

"I wonder if there are any left somewhere else in here?" questioned Bobby as he began to look around.

"There could be, but watch your—"

I didn't get it out of my mouth before Bobby disappeared down a rather large rabbit hole. You see? This was exactly why I brought the ropes. I knew by a diagram that I had seen from a civil war buff that there very likely was such a hole that actually went down below the river bed.

I went over to the hole to see if I could spy Bobby, but couldn't. The hole had enough of a bend to make him invisible to me except for his headlight. However, I sure did hear him! He was quite all right, other than being a bit pissed off. He had stopped on a slight ledge.

"Kavin, it's too slick for me to climb up!"

"Can you put your feet against the wall and jimmy your way up?"

"NO! It's too narrow!"

"Hold on, Bobby, I'll get the ropes."

I returned quickly and threw the first one down.

"Can you see the rope?"

"NO!"

"How far down are you?"

"At least sixty feet!"

"Holy shit!"

That was a little above the distance to the foot of the hill and deeper than the length of both of my ropes.

"How much deeper does the hole look?"

"I can't tell, but it looks pretty deep. It also appears to get slightly wider farther down."

"I'm going to tie my other rope to the end of this one and drop it on down."

I did just that, but my two twenty-five foot ropes were two feet too short. He wasn't as deep as he thought.

"Well hell!" exclaimed Bobby.

"Hold on a little longer, Bobby. I'll go to the shop and get another rope. Can you hold on for an hour? Maybe less?"

"Damn it, Kavin! You're supposed to say, 'Can you hold on for a half hour? Maybe just a little more.' 'Cause it always takes longer than you think!"

"You're right . . . you're right . . . I'll get back as fast as I can."

I gathered my wits—there wasn't much else I could gather— and carefully left the mausoleum. When I got to the bridge, I was shocked to see Bobby's twin standing there! Except that it really was Bobby! I noticed that his pants were wet to the knees.

"How in the world did you get here?"

"I accidently slid down about ten more feet and found another tunnel. Looks like it was man-made too. It descends slightly down to an exit just at the water's edge. It sits in like a little alcove, which is good. Because of the brush, nobody's gonna see it."

Just then an ambulance's scream pierced the calm. We knew its cargo. Another came closely behind it, along with three cop cars.

We were mortified, but they paid us no heed. Bobby and I expelled our collective breath when we knew for certain that they were ignoring us. I figured that if I were to survive this, then I could survive anything. My heart had been racing for the better part of an hour now. My mouth was dry and my adrenaline was running low.

I asked Bobby what he wanted to do next. He hesitated for a moment and sighed. I was never used to Bobby hesitating, but he did. I didn't know if he was giving up or if he was thinking of a way to finish this thing. He looked over his shoulder at the cemetery. He had a look of determination in his eye. I believe that I was even more determined than he was.

I was getting tired and I was getting thirsty. I suggested to Bobby that we should go get something to drink. Water was something that we never figured on. We figured that we could just get in and out. You know the old saying, "To assume [which is like figuring] is making an ass out of you and me."

We walked down Main Street and found a convenience store. After we paid for our water, we went outside and discussed what to do next. Bobby said that he believed there was a relatively large cavern below where he left the tunnel. He thought that if we went in where he came out at the river's edge, then we could use my ropes to drop down into the cavern.

So we had to go back to the mausoleum to retrieve the ropes. We were not as cautious this go round as we were the first. However, we got to the mausoleum with no problem. We re-entered the mausoleum and retrieved the ropes and headed to the river.

Flashlights in hand, we moved into the alcove and into the knee-deep water and then into the cave. We had to hunch down as we walked up the tunnel, but it was a breeze compared to what we had already been through. I did manage to bump my head a couple of times but rejoiced at the idea that my years of stick-in-the-muditudiness were coming to an end.

I didn't give a damn about the gold. I really didn't believe it was there. After all, my history suggested—*no*—stated with no doubts that I was to fail. Again doubt. You see that was burned into my brain. But then again I was with Bobby. He never had any doubts. Regardless of my expectations, I was on an endorphin high.

We quickly got to the intersection of the tunnels. I shined my light downward and was surprised at the ambiance of a yellowish glow. We both knew what it had to be, so we joyously threw down one of the ropes, and I, for once in a very long time, agreed to go first. Of course since there was nothing to tie the rope to, Bobby had to hold onto it and lower me down.

It was not nearly as far down as we thought and I landed quite hard. At first I thought I sprained my ankle and was momentarily disinterested in our material pursuit. I had landed on a rock and quickly discovered that the floor was covered in very thick silt. I looked intently around and noticed a pool of water that was around six feet in diameter.

"Bobby, I don't see anything down here except a bunch of trash that must have floated in here when the river got high. I believe what we found up above is all there is," I shouted. "That yellowish glow is just a bunch of beer bottles. Damn! There's a Wonder Bread wrapper!"

"Dammit, Kavin! You don't have to shout! You know you're standing at the end of a damn *huge megaphone!*"

"Oops," I whispered. "Well . . . Anyway I don't see anything," I said as I limped around.

Suddenly my toe caught the corner of something that made a thump. I bent down and dug the silt and garbage away from the corner of a metal chest. I became invigorated by this discovery and began digging much the way a prairie dog does and uncovered the lid.

There was a very old iron padlock standing guard against any intrusion. I was a little miffed and kicked the hell out of it, which to my surprise, sent it sailing across the cavern. Bobby wanted to know what was going on so I announced that I had found a relic that very well could be containing something related to treasure.

"I'm coming down."

"Bobby! How in the hell are we going to get out if you come down?"

"Yeah, I guess you're right. What have you found?"

"I've found a trunk of some kind buried in the silt."

"Hell bells and fuzzy feet! You don't say! Can you open it?"

"I don't know yet. Have you got your little pry bar?"

It nearly hit me as it flew past my head! I picked it up and went to work on the chest, and though it creaked and groaned, it grudgingly complied. There it was!

It was a metal box full of rust and silt and not much else. Of course, first impressions are not always right. I dug my fingers into the silt and determined that, indeed, there appeared to be coins. As one might imagine, I became somewhat excited. I was so excited that I actually sneezed. I would have been truly embarrassed if Bobby had known my story.

"What's the matter, Kavin? You got a girl down there?"

Looks like he knew my story.

"It's musty down here, *asshole*!"

"Whatever . . . What's with the box?"

"Well . . . it appears that there are some things that closely resemble the shape of possible coins. At this point, owing to the fact that I have not dug any of them out, I must point out that I can only speculate as to what these shapes are."

Of course, I was stupidly giddy. I had never been as intoxicated by libations as I was by the prospect of no more monetary worries. Bobby was getting anxious and was showing no sense of humor. Of course I always picked out the worst times to try to be funny.

"Kevin, dig some of those coins out! I know that is what you have found!"

"You're right, Bobby! They are definitely coins, but they are tarnished. They aren't gold. They look like they're silver . . . The years look right though. Hey! You just called me Kevin."

"Dammit, just keep digging. I still bet there are gold coins in there somewhere."

"Yeah . . . I found some! Definitely gold. Throw me the bags."

"What bags?"

"Quit kidding! Didn't you bring the burlap bags?"

"I thought you said you brought them!"

"You're kidding, right!"

He: "Fuck!"

Me: "Fuck!!"

He: "FUCKING HELL!"

"I knew that we weren't ready, Bobby! We have never done any-thing like this in all our days! Or have you?"

"That's a discussion for another day, Kavin. Listen, I'll pull you back up and we'll go back up top to get our stuff and hide our tracks. We'll leave the rope. In the meantime we better at least put the crypt door back in."

"Bobby, we won't be able come back tomorrow because we won't be able to find a hardware store open that sells burlap bags. Besides that, my wife already has plans," I said after he pulled me up.

"Yeah, we don't need to rush this thing at this point. Let's gather our wits until New Year's Eve . . . We've already made enough mis-takes. Wish we could go on and get this shit out of here though!"

"Ah hell! It's been in here well over a hundred years. It ain't going nowhere!"

So that was our plan. You know how plans are. How could we have expected a not-so-well-laid-out plan to work when well-laid-out plans often go awry?

We got back to our vehicles muddy and tired. We just looked at each other and collectively sighed. We shook hands and told each other "Merry Christmas." We agreed to call one another the next day but we wouldn't be able to see each other due to family obligations. As they say, "There was no joy in Mudville."

I didn't know how Bobby felt, but I felt dead. The gold was right there in my hands. Of course I had loaded my pockets with as much gold as I could get in them, which was around two hundred coins. I gave Bobby approximately half the haul, which made him fairly happy. Somehow I felt that that was as close as I was going to get.

I went by the shop to change clothes, and by the time I got home, it was starting to rain. My wife met me at the door and leaned forward for a kiss and noticed a strange odor. My answer was vague but she pretended that it didn't bother her.

We talked of plans for tomorrow and how excited she was, but I had real trouble feigning excitement. Exhausted, I went to bed and fell asleep but awoke two hours later agonizing over the night's disaster. I tried not to toss and turn, but I still woke up my wife. She asked me what my problem was and I replied that I had too much sugar at Paul's house where I supposedly was to help him and his wife put out his kids' presents.

It rained hard all day Christmas and the day after Christmas and the day after the day after Christmas . . . New Year's Eve! The water was already too high to get in! It rained until January the third. I could only imagine just how high the water had risen inside the cavern. I intended to go into the mausoleum with enough rope to lower myself down far enough to investigate the water.

On the fourth of January, I rode over to Rose Hill and parked above the Warren mausoleum and walked down to the front of it. I was investigating where Bobby and I had cut the gate and saw that our little folly was a little more obvious than what we had thought when I heard a truck coming around the narrow drive. It was the sexton of the cemetery and his helper. I had to step back onto the embankment to avoid being hit by the truck.

"Well . . . Mr. Kevin, what brings you here on this fine soggy day?"

"Well, hey George . . . Dad said that he heard there was some mischief going on over here at the Warren mausoleum, so I thought I'd check it out. What do you reckon was going on?"

"Kev, it looks like somebody tried to break in here, but it doesn't look like they got in. All hell broke loose Christmas Eve night so they might have gotten scared off before they did."

"Really? What happened?"

"Don't tell anybody"—which is what he always said whenever he was about to spill the beans about stuff that nobody at the city wanted the public to know—"the sheriff and one of our judges was buck naked a floatin' down the river and they nearly drowned! They had been at a party but somebody who was there said that they disappeared together and figured that they must've gone on over to Rose Hill and were doing the pattycake together! You know there's lots of folks that come up here to do it up on top of this here mausoleum? Who knows? Whoever was trying to get in down here might have scared them off and them getting scared off too."

"Well anyway, I'm glad the vandals didn't do too much damage. It pisses me off every time somebody breaks into one of these mausoleums."

"Yeah, me too . . . Ol' Ron Gilbert is coming over here to see if he can make this thing more difficult to get into. He's talking about using some harder bolts or something."

"I don't know, George, but do you think there might have been some sort of devil worship thing going on?"

"Who the hell knows these days!"

"Guess I better get back to work. See you later, George."

"Yeah, Kev, see you later."

The fact is that I was born with a guilty conscience and so I'm not sure how cool I really was in front of George. If he suspected anything of me, he didn't show it. Even though it was only thirty-eight degrees I was sweating profusely and my mouth was dry. When I got back to my truck, I started to shake very slightly. I knew that there was no way in hell that I would not break under pressure.

After I calmed down, I realized that the goal of corralling the gold was nearly gone. I telephoned Bobby to tell him what was going on, to which he replied, "Oh well."

***

It seemed like that every time the water began to recede, we would get another round of rain and the level would rise again. This went on for two months and I spent way too much time watching the water go up and down. The more time that I spent down by the river, the less time that I was spending with my wife. My obsessing over the gold was ruining my marriage and I didn't even know it.

March came and the rains finally stopped and my attitude became more intense. I watched every day as the waters receded. Finally, by the tenth of March, the water was low enough for me to go into the cave at the alcove. The problem was that there was an old fisherman standing on the riverbank not more than fifty feet away! I didn't want him to see me disappearing behind the bushes and not coming out for a while so I went home. I would have to go back the next day.

My wife informed me that evening when I got home that the next day we were going to go out and that I was not to be late coming home after work. She must have seen the panic in my eyes because she gave me a really nasty look. I shook off my panic and smiled as sincerely as I could.

I decided that now was the time to tell her what I had been up to. She reached for the candy dish! I knew where it was going; she always threw the baseball high and to my right . . . This was not a baseball. I tried to duck low and to the left, which is exactly where the dish went!

I came to with a bloody rag and a bag of frozen butter peas pressed against my forehead. My wife came into the room with a fresh rag and checked my head.

"Looks like stitches to me," she said.

"Blasted!" I blurted. "Why in Hades did you do that?"

"What in the world makes you think that I would believe a cockamamie story like that?"

"Because it's the truth! I can prove it! Go look in the can where I keep my loose change. You'll find some strange-looking coins."

She left the room, and when she came back, she was very rigid. She was gathering her thoughts, and when it appeared that she knew what she was going to say, she just screamed!

"You're a freaking criminal, Kevin!"

"But I did it for you! I was thinking of you the whole time!" But of course I wasn't. I was thinking about that E-type Jaguar that I was going to buy.

"We better get you to the doctor to stitch you up. You're starting to bleed on my pillow!"

232

Up until that point I had really liked fiery women.

**

I cashed in my coins at three different pawnshops in other towns and came away with $2,500, which was way less than what they were worth, but I had no choice. None of the proprietors asked me any questions, but one of them cut his eyes up at me while he was examining the coins as though he knew exactly what they were.

I moved into an apartment. I didn't like it. My parents couldn't understand what happened. "You know how those fiery redheads are," I said. Well, at least I could go get some more gold and have a comfortable life.

I called Bobby and told him how much money I got for my coins. He got about the same. I told him I was ready to go back and that I had not been able to watch the scene very closely for about a week. He arrived Friday evening and was fired up to tackle the task again.

We left my apartment at 2:00 AM and were walking down the riverbank toward the alcove at 2:30 AM. This time we had plenty of rope and a grappling hook. We also had actual spelunker's hats and a bunch of burlap bags.

The tunnel had become slippery due to the recent deposit of fresh silt. We got to the drop-off, secured our hook, and this time Bobby went down . . . that damn laugh of his!

"What is it!?" I asked anxiously.

"It's gone!"

"What's gone?"

"The fucking gold is what's gone!"

"Bullshit!" I said as I let myself down.

Yep, he wasn't pulling my leg.

I slid down the rope and, indeed, the gold was gone. How?

"Bobby! Look over there!"

There was a mound of dirt created by an obvious hole that uncovered another tunnel that was wide enough to drag trunks of gold through that had been hidden by a round piece of marble! We jolted for the opening and wound up in a very old brick culvert that drained out into the river that nobody paid any attention to. It was in a perfect place to get the gold out.

If anyone was near the riverbank, they were probably scared shitless by the macabre laughter and the intense cursing coming from the two of us. I'm sure that we could be heard from the police station.

We got ourselves out, and when we got onto firm footing, we threw our stuff in the river. I watched hopelessly as the burlap bags floated away and gently began to sink, my hope for a better life sinking with it.

We walked along the riverbank holding hands to throw off the cops who were coming our way. Once the cops got past and we returned to being heterosexual, I had a horrible thought.

"Bobby, what if, whoever took that gold were some really bad characters? If we had not screwed up and left we might be dead."

Bobby was obviously thinking hard about what I said and took a minute or so to reply.

"You know, Kavin, I bet that old musket and that Confederate soldier are worth a lot of money."

"FUCK THAT CONFEDERATE SOLDIER!"

***

Serendipity-do-dah

Many years later . . .

Craig and I had just returned from the cemetery, and when we entered the office, my father was sitting on the couch with a grave look on his face that was reminiscent of his look that he had when he told us that two planes had flown into the Twin Towers in New York City. I knew from his look that there was really bad news. I kept quiet to allow him to speak first.

I had one of those feelings all day long that something bad had happened. I had a reprieve from the feeling for about an hour before we got back to the shop, but when I went in the office door and saw my father, I knew it had been real.

"I've got some bad news . . . They found Barry lying on the ground dead."

"Do they know what happened? Did he kill himself?"

"I don't know what happened to him. I just heard about it from Jimmy Casey when I ate lunch at the diner."

"Who's Jimmy Casey?"

"You know, he works with Barry's boss."

"So he really didn't know anything?"

"No, he gave me his boss's phone number, if you want to call to find out what happened."

I looked at the phone number, but it was just a blur. I wasn't ready to face this. I knew that it was coming, but like everyone else, I buried this eventuality deep in the recesses of my mind. Many thoughts raced through my head and none of them were pleasant. At first I was angry, then I was sad, and then I became indifferent. *To hell with him*, I thought.

I put the phone number back down on the desk and went back down to the shop to work. Even though I tried to block Barry from my mind, I kept seeing his face and many questions kept gnawing at me. My angst got the better of me and I retrieved the phone number and made the call.

I was surprised by the jovial air of Barry's boss. I was also surprised to find out that it was not suicide. Evidently Barry had sat down at the base of the resort's flagpole during a thunder storm. I suddenly felt guilty for judging him.

After work I drove up to the resort to investigate, which for me was a way to connect time and space and to live that last moment with Barry. His dog meandered up to me; no one had bothered to take him. I saw where Barry had been sitting and noticed a burn mark where his rear end must have been. I also saw his shoes, which he never tied, that must have been blown off his feet.

Instinctively, I stepped off the distance from the flagpole to each shoe and discovered that they were thirty feet from the pole and thirty feet from each other. *Weird*, I thought.

I looked down at Sycamore the dog, who was aptly named because Barry would always sic him on runners who got too close to his cabin.

"Sycamore, where were you boy when this happened?"

Sycamore just stood wagging his tail, looking at me with his bright eyes and his tongue hanging out. I wasn't sure what I was going to do with him, but I knew that I could not leave him. I started to walk toward Barry's cabin to see if anyone had left him food. Over in the vinca, a small book, its open pages facing down, caught my eye.

When I got closer to it, I knew that it was Barry's life ledger, or diary if you will. I called it a ledger because when he was in our employ, he would write everything down in one of his many little ledger books as though he were cataloging his life.

I took the book along with Sycamore down to the cabin and went inside to read it. The cabin was locked, but I had two keys that Barry had given me for "just in case."

I was in the realm of the surreal. I was feeling an inexplicable presence. My hands worked independently from my mind and opened the book. I automatically went to the last pages and saw that, indeed, he was recording his last moment on earth.

June 15

-what an awesome day went for walk with Sycamore went 14 miles- not bad Sycamore is getting slow need to give him fish oil and glucosamin am feeling the best I have in years I feel awesome thunderstorm north of here looks like it's going around Sycamore keeps barking I think he's hungry I miss my mother she's been gone two years now think I'll call K-----

That's where it stopped. It looked like his pencil skidded across the page. Was he going to call me, or was he going to call Katie? Doesn't matter. He couldn't call either of us.

I laid the keys down on the kitchen counter because I wouldn't need them anymore. The gate at the far end of the road from the resort was electronic and would open automatically to go out. I needed a physical key to get in because Barry wouldn't give me the code to the keypad. I gathered Sycamore's dish, his bag of food, and Sycamore and with Barry's diary in hand went back to the truck and drove home.

About a month later, I got a letter from a lawyer's office. I didn't even know that Barry had a will. The letter informed me that I had been named as his sole heir. I knew that his mother had left him an inheritance, but he had used a large portion of it to fund a scholarship at the college.

I was shown a seat in the lawyer's office by his secretary, and a few minutes later, a very amiable man entered the room and extended his hand. We shook hands very firmly, which I didn't expect. The lawyer seemed excited, which was very puzzling to me. The few lawyers I had ever come into contact with always had the aura of dead fish.

"Mr. Sanders?"

"Yes, sir."

"I'm Wcldvkbekcyeckg." I forgot his name as soon he said it. "You have been left a large sum of money by Mr. Barry M. McStotts blah blah blah blah blah blah blah blah blah blah blah."

For a while I didn't hear anything else he said. I was in a daze. I did hear the amount of $685,000. The image of a 1964 E-type Jaguar racing down a country road came into my head.

At the end of the appointment the lawyer handed me an envelope containing a letter. I waited until I got a home to read it:

Kevin,

If you are reading this, then you know I am dead, ha-ha! For some reason I always figured that I would live to be an old man. Maybe that's why I tried to do what I did all of those times. You know that I have never feared death. Whether I am in Valhala or not, should not concern you. There are many things that I need to tell you. One thing is that I was adopted and I hate my adopted sister so that is why I am leaving you my "fortune." My real father's name was Horace Dempsey. My real mother's name was Evelyn Warren. She was only fourteen when I was conceived. My real father would have gone to jail in today's time, but you know how it was back then. A few years ago, I was in a pizza place and overheard you talking to a friend about the mausoleum. I was sitting in the booth right behind you and you never even saw me. It kind of ticked me off that you didn't trust me enough to include me in on your treasure hunt. That was my ancestor's mausoleum. I knew about the tunnel, including the one that went in from the river. Me and Tommy actually went in that cavern where the gold was when we were teenagers, but hell, we didn't know there was gold in there. I was hiding in the shadows when you guys broke into the mausoleum and later saw you disappear into the riverbank so I knew where you were going. Boy! I thought that I was goofy! At any rate, after you all left and the sirens died down that night, I stole the city's big pontoon boat and anchored it just outside the tunnel at the edge of the river. After I got most of the gold and silver that was in that little cavern, which by the way could not have been even close to what the Confederates actually had—regardless it was a pretty fair amount, some of it is still in there but I threw it into a pool of water—I floated down the river and anchored at the mouth of the creek that was next to my parents' old home place. I knew a great hiding place and that is where I hid the gold. It took me several years to cash it all in. Do you remember that I always had a lot of cash on me? You thought I was getting it from my mother. Ha ha! Well, you know the rest of the story. I don't know how much money is left. After all, you know I'll spend it as long as I'm alive, but if there is any left, I know you'll put it to good use. You're awesome. PS you may wonder what I used to get the gold out with—Tupperware! Don't ask me how much I used.

I was flabbergasted! It was no surprise to me that he had commandeered the city's boat. I still don't know why he always said that I was awesome. I never felt any more than ordinary, but he always said it with great conviction. I really didn't want to let my family know what I had just inherited.

Of course what really flabbergasted me was that Barry's real father's name was the same as Bobby's. No wonder! It did answer a lot of questions about how much alike they were. It also made me wonder just how demented Mr. Dempsey must have been! I thought about telling Bobby, but then again, what good would that do? He was doing well enough financially anyway, and wouldn't the stress of knowing that he had a half-brother, who was now deceased, be worth $342,500 not to have to deal with it? I wondered too if Barry knew that he had two brothers.

I invested some, but I put most of it in three different bank accounts and slowly began to rebuild the shop. I bought a house, and a couple of years later, my dad joined the Democratic Party upon their discovery of his death. (That's what some say, anyway.)

Near the same time I went out to the college to attend the dedication for the statue of Barry and his dog (it didn't look anything like his physical self, but the sculptor did seem to catch his maniacal self). Turns out he donated a hell of a lot of money to the school, which is the reason they never fired him!

I didn't buy the 1964 E-type Jaguar. It was too much money and that's why I bought those two fifties model MGs. I never liked being too conspicuous. So the spirit world made sure that I still didn't have enough money to retire early, thus my life goes on. As the late great Barry McStotts used to say when I was getting too picky about setting a monument: "Well enough!"

***

Just One Last Thing

Five miles down the road, ten miles from the cemetery of the day, I heard it too often. It was my brother. He had to pee.

"I've got to pee."

"I thought you went before we left."

"No, I didn't pee!"

"Well, why didn't you?"

"I didn't have to go then! I have to go now!"

Wasn't this the same thing that went on when we were kids? He was always the one that had to go pee as soon as we got ten minutes down the road. It's no wonder that my mother stayed so frazzled all the time! Are you kidding? Five children in the car at the same time, and like dominoes, our bladders would begin to fall.

Of course, the other four of us wouldn't even be thinking about it until he said, "I've got to pee!" Once he blurted it out, it was too late for the rest of us; the floodgates would open. There weren't a lot of public restrooms in those days and the ones that were available were always at these nasty service stations, but that's where my mother would take us. Yes! On purpose!

These stations' restrooms were so nasty that the bugs left them alone. But don't empty your bladder at home and get what's coming to you! We learned after too long a time. Better not drink sweet tea or colas before you get in Mom's car.

I felt like the same rule should apply at work, but my brother never cared for rules. However, I was driving and I wasn't going to pull over on this narrow-ass road just to let him pee.

"I've really got to pee!"

"Look! There's hardly anywhere around here I can pull off and there are no convenience stores between here and the cemetery that

241

have restrooms. We are nine miles out and you can pee in the woods when we get to the cemetery."

So he calmed down and started looking at his iPhone, which took his mind off his predicament and got me to thinking about an article that I read the day before.

"You know the NSA and the FBI and who knows who else can track a person everywhere they go just by their iPhone or any other mobile device."

"Who cares? I'm not doing anything."

"They can tell where you are by your phone pinging off the cell towers. And even if you turn it off or take the battery out, the capacitors in that thing keep it active until they discharge. So if they want to, they can go right into that phone and tell exactly where you are. Not only that, they can even hear everything we say."

"Still why do they care?"

"Because they want to know who you are and what you do and who you're doing it with, because they don't have anything else better to do."

"So why don't they track terrorists then? Or drug dealers or other people that need to be tracked?"

"You know I've been thinking about that. I believe it's because terrorists don't pay taxes and probably don't have a bank account in their name . . . It's easier to go after honest people. They want to track taxpayers so they'll know where we're spending our money. Then they'll seize our bank accounts."

"That's why I don't have one."

"Yeah well, then they'll outlaw cash. The other thing . . . Terrorists and drug dealers, most of them anyway, use burn phones."

"Who cares? I'm not doing anything."

I was just trying to get into his head. Next time he goes to buy pot he'll probably be looking over his shoulder or he'll leave his phone at home.

Meanwhile, we got a little closer to the cemetery and his complaints started again.

"What you want me to do about it? Look at all these houses around here. Look, we go around three more curves and we're at the churh and there's plenty of woods to go in!"

His body language left no doubt that he was in agony, but as I said . . . We made the next three turns and what do you think we found? How did you know? The woods were gone and there were houses everywhere!

Obviously we hadn't been to this particular cemetery in a long while. My brother was a little on the wild side and he didn't really care that there were houses around, so he jumped out of the truck and commenced to pee but still remained somewhat pissed.

He got even more pissed off twenty minutes later when the police rolled up. Some old lady had been looking out of her window, probably trying to see if we were perhaps gravediggers getting a grave ready for one of her friends. And yes, she called the police when he took to peeing.

My brother was lucky. The cop was a friend of ours and laughed it off. He went to talk to the lady and confused her so completely with some kind of made-up police jargon that she simply forgot what it was that she called the police for in the first place!

When we finished our task, we got in the truck and headed for home, which gave my brother occasion to simmer down. However, he was still pissed and commented, "What really tics me off is, nowadays, if I self-identify as a girl, I can take PE with them and go shower with them, pee, scratch, whatever . . . but I can't even take a piss out in nature any more!"

"Maybe next time you self-identify as a dog and hike your leg and pee on a tire . . ."

"I think that's a damn good idea!"

"You know, I think I'll write a story about a guy who self-identifies as a chicken and he gets eaten by his neighbor, and when they arrest the guy and take him to court the judge throws it out because the 'chicken's' family shows up struttin', peckin', an' cluckin' . . . Case closed!"

DÄCH PHILLUPS

Rows and rows of houses
as far as the eye can see.
Not even a pitiful little bush
to go behind and pee!

How Much Does That Weigh?

Question: How much does that weigh? Answer: A lot.

Question: Where do you get your granite poured? Answer: It's not poured; it comes out of the ground in these big old blocks. (What we really want to say: we pour it ourselves after we take a hammer to this great huge block and pulverize it into dust, then we mix it with Portland cement and fairy dust and then inject it into this mold and jump up and down on it until it gets really hard.)

Question: How long does it take you to chisel out the letters on a tombstone? Answer: Probably a really long time since we don't know how to chisel letters anymore and it would take years to learn.

Question: Do y'all use some kind of acid or something to letter those stones? Answer: No, when one uses acid, it is hard to do anything but enjoy the trip.

Question: Which stone is your favorite? Answer: Whichever one that sells.

Question: But if you had to choose your favorite what would it be? Answer: It would be the one that makes the most money after we sell it.

Question: But when it's your time to get a tombstone, which one would you choose? Answer: Personally I would just as soon not have a tombstone because you know what that means.

Question: Okay, so what would you pick out for your mother? Answer: If you're basing your decision on what stone I would buy for my mother, I would have to say the absolute most expensive stone that I could find that will make me the most money.

Question: Do you think this six hundred-pound monument will fit in the trunk of my car? Answer: Sure, it will! But we're not gonna put it in there.

Question: Why not? Answer: ^$&^%$*^%^%$@!

Serious question: How long have you been doing this? Answer: A really long time.

Question: How many tombstones have you set? Answer: Tons.

Question: No, seriously, how many stones have you set? Answer: Tons and tons.

Question: If you had a dollar for every tombstone you ever set, how much money would you have? Answer: Way more than enough to retire on and live a life of luxury. (This is very depressing because the reality is: this means we didn't even make a dollar a stone.)

Question: How did you get into this business? Answer: Sort of by accident. You would know if you hadn't skipped to the end. Read the book!

Question: How many times do people ask you how much their stone weighs? Answer: Nearly every single time.

Question: What is the single most often asked question about your business? Answer: How much does that weigh?

Question: If you could have done anything else with your life besides tombstones what would it be? Answer: Write a fucking book!

Buh-bye now!

CPSIA information can be obtained
at www.ICGtesting.com
Printed in the USA
FFHW020852060319
50890273-56294FF